The Burgess Book of Nature Lore

Adventures of Tommy, Sue, and Sammy
with Their Friends
of Meadow, Pool, and Forest

by

THORNTON W. BURGESS

Illustrated by Robert Candy

BONANZA BOOKS · NEW YORK

LIBRARY OF CONGRESS CATALOG CARD NO. 65-10581

This edition published by Bonanza Books,
a division of Crown Publishers, Inc.,
by arrangement with Little, Brown and Company
c d e f g h

PRINTED IN THE UNITED STATES OF AMERICA

Contents

Contents

1

Vacation Frustration

"It's hateful!" cried Sue, her black eyes stormy and wet with disappointment and temper. She stamped a foot angrily.

Her twin brother Sammy grinned. It was a rueful sort of grin. "I feel the same as you do but there's nothing we can do about it. Father just has to go at this time, and I am glad Mother is going with him. She will have a wonderful time and she needs the change."

"I'm glad of that too," agreed Sue. "Of course I am. But it is just too bad for us."

"It does upset all our plans and it has come like a regular missile bomb out of nowhere. I suppose we can stand it for one summer. We've just got to," said Sammy.

For as many of their twelve years as they could remember the twins had spent each summer at the seashore, and they loved it there. All through the past winter they had planned what they would do this summer at the beach. Now this devastating blow fell on all their plans and dreams. It had come without warning. Unexpected and important business was taking Father abroad for a couple of months, and Mother was going with him. The cottage at the beach was to be rented, and the twins were to spend the summer with their Uncle Dick and Aunt Em and cousin Tommy, who lived on a farm at the foot of the White Mountains. The twins never had been out in the country to stay, for they lived in the city in winter and at the beach in summer.

"I wonder if when Tommy visited us he felt about the city as we do about the country," said Sue.

"He couldn't," Sammy declared. "He just couldn't. In the city there is always something going on, something doing, something to see. But out there on the farm what is there to do, I ask you? We'll just — stagnate."

Sue laughed. She was once more her usual good-natured self, though far from happy. "Whatever that means, I guess we will," said she. "I guess it's going to be pretty stupid. No water skiing, and I love water skiing. All winter I've dreamed what

fun it was going to be behind that new speedboat
of Bill Whitcomb's. Now there won't be any."

"Nor any boat racing," said Sammy.

"Nor sailing!" cried Sue.

"Nor skin diving," added Sammy.

"No swimming matches," moaned Sue.

"Nor crabbing," said Sammy.

"No clambakes," wailed Sue.

Both of them laughed and felt better. "I suppose we'll find something to do up there," said Sue.

"We can play with the calves and the pigs and
the chickens," said Sammy.

"And don't forget Tommy. You know we both
liked him when he was here," said Sue.

"That's true," replied Sammy. "He was interested in a lot of things that he was seeing for the
first time, but I guess we won't have any such luck.
I guess he won't have much of interest to show us.
Darned if I know what we're going to do for a
little excitement once in a while."

"Play croquet," teased Sue.

Sammy threw a sofa pillow at his sister. "That's
it," said he. "You're probably nearer right than I
like to think you are. Exciting, isn't it? You may
as well put away your tennis racket right now unless you just want to bat balls against the barn door.

Know something, Sis? It's three miles on a dirt road, then three back. Six miles to get a Coke."

"Anyway, there's a TV and Tommy said it's a good one. I'm glad of that," said Sue.

"Me too," growled Sammy. "At least I can watch a ball game now and then, thank goodness. Probably that's all the excitement I'll get." He spoke bitterly.

"Perhaps we'll see a bear. That would be exciting. You know the name of the mountain right back of the farm is Bear Knob," contributed Sue.

"Huh! That doesn't mean there are any bears there now. All the bears you'll see, if any, will be a teddy bear some kids have left around," retorted Sammy. "Know what I think?"

"I'm not interested," replied Sue. "I don't care what you think."

"I think it's going to be a stupid summer," said Sammy and resumed packing a bag.

"Maybe we'll be surprised," said Sue, but she didn't sound as if she believed that. "Maybe we'll see a moose. You know Tommy wrote that a bull moose had been seen in the neighborhood several times."

"I'd rather see a whale," grumbled Sammy and grinned.

[6]

"Or a shark or a seal," Sue added, and she also grinned. They were rueful grins.

"Let's forget it and get packed," growled Sammy.

The next day the hundred-and-eighty-mile ride through lovely country that was new to them would distract their thoughts until they met a car with a boat in tow. At sight of this a new wave of home-sickness and frustration would cast a shadow that for the time being dimmed the brightness of the day. They were sure that each of those boats was headed for the seashore. Of course many of them, perhaps a majority, were headed for inland waters.

As they passed around the foot of a lake a speed-boat swung in a great arc close to shore. Behind it was a girl on water skis, a picture of athletic grace and skill and thrilling excitement. It brought a lump into Sue's throat. This was her favorite sport, and it looked now as if she would have to forego it completely for this season. She turned her face as she tried to swallow the lump so that Sammy would not see her momentary misery.

A little later they passed another lake, where a race of small sailboats was in progress, and it was Sammy's turn to feel that overwhelming sense of frustration. He loved sailing, and he was expert at handling small boats.

Shortly before they reached the farm a doe bounded across the road only a few feet in front of them. She stopped and turned to stare at them, her great soft eyes filled with suspicion and curiosity. Then, as Father brought the car to a full stop, she bounded away, her white tail a bobbing white spot that steadily grew smaller until it vanished in the brush at the edge of a strip of woodland.

Sue clapped her hands in delight. "That's a sign of good luck!" she cried happily. "I just know it! Perhaps now we'll see a bear or a moose. Wouldn't that be exciting?"

"I still would rather see a whale," said Sammy with a wry grin.

They got to the farm early in the afternoon. The warm welcome from Uncle Dick, Aunt Em and Tommy served to dissipate the blues for the time being. Afterward they said farewell to Father, who was returning to the city at once, for he and Mother were to sail at midnight the following day. Then followed a get-acquainted inspection tour of the barn, the poultry house, the workshop and the sheds and the mechanized equipment, some of which was completely new to the twins. Uncle Dick was up to date in mechanized farming and the farm was well equipped with planting and harvesting machinery. This was of special interest to Sammy, who was mechanically inclined.

The orchard with its row of beehives was visited. Also the garden, of which Tommy was very proud, since it was his special charge. They were introduced to the young prize Black Angus bull he was raising and grooming daily for entry in the 4–H Club contests at the coming fall fairs. Sue quite lost her heart to a roan colt whose dam was a fine saddle horse. Tommy assured her she should ride whenever she chose. This would be next best to riding the skis behind Bill Whitcomb's speedboat, perhaps even more fun.

The picturesque old farmhouse dated back nearly two hundred years. It had been delightfully modernized without losing any of its charm and interest. In fact, it was more comfortable and better furnished and equipped than the twins' own home at the beach. The moment they stepped into the long living room they had that wonderfully satisfying "at home" feeling. Sammy's keen eyes at once spotted the TV, and he noted with satisfaction that it was the same make and model as the one at

home, one of the very best. He noted, too, a catcher's mitt lying on a chair. Could it be that Tommy was a ballplayer? Perhaps the summer wouldn't be so bad after all.

That night the twins went to bed in a far happier frame of mind than they had started out with in the morning. As Sue dropped off to sleep she was dimly aware that something was missing. It was the sound of waves breaking on the shore. Here all was still, so very, very still. "But I like it," she whispered to herself.

In the next room Sammy was wondering if Uncle Dick would let him drive the tractor. He had a feeling that he would.

2

The Testing of a Friend

That first morning was a lovely one, and Sue was out early exploring the dooryard.

"Who digs a hole and carts off all the sand from it?" she asked Tommy.

"Is that a conundrum? I'm no good at conundrums. I'll bite. Who does?" replied Tommy.

"It isn't a conundrum. It's a puzzle and I want to know the answer," retorted Sue.

"She's found a little hole out in the lawn. I think it's a snake's hole," put in Sammy.

"It goes straight down, and there isn't a grain of sand left around it," added Sue.

"Show me," said Tommy.

Sue did. It was a small hole, little more than an inch and a half across. It went straight down for perhaps a foot and a half, and either ended abruptly or made a sharp turn — Sue wasn't sure which. It was in the open lawn several feet out from the shrubbery by the house.

"How can a hole that size be dug and not a grain of sand left outside it? It doesn't seem possible. Even the teeny-weeny holes of the ants have little piles of sand around them," said Sue.

Tommy was on his knees examining the hole. "This hole wasn't here a few days ago when I mowed the lawn," said he. He looked up with a quizzical expression. "Do you know anyone around here with pockets in his cheeks?" he asked.

"Striped Chipmunk! Tommy, do you mean you think Striped Chipmunk dug this hole? He can't have. Last night when I asked you if there was a chipmunk about, you told me that he was living under the old stone wall." Sue was excited.

"Ever change your mind, Sue? Perhaps Striped Chipmunk changed his and moved over here. Anyway, if he didn't dig this hole one of his family did. I know a chipmunk's hole when I see it," asserted Tommy.

"It's the pockets in his cheeks," Sammy broke in.

"What in the world are you talking about?" Sue demanded.

"He carried away the sand in his pockets. That's

the reason there's none around his hole," declared Sammy.

"No, he didn't! No, he didn't!" Sue was dancing with excitement. "I've just remembered something I read. A chipmunk starts to dig a home in some more or less hidden place. He pushes the sand out behind him just as Johnny Chuck does. When he has the new home dug he makes a new entrance some distance from the old one. He opens it from the inside, pushing the sand back through the tunnel and out of the first doorway. Then he closes this by packing it full of sand, and uses the new doorway with no telltale sand on the doorstep. Isn't that it, Tommy?" Sue had talked so fast she was out of breath.

"Stupid, if you ask me, to make his home right out in the open," said Sammy.

"Smart!" Tommy contradicted. "He knows folks are not likely to look for it out here."

"Do animals really think, or do they do everything by instinct?" asked Sue.

Tommy grinned. "If an animal did everything by instinct I wouldn't call anything it did, however remarkable, being smart," said he. "Some animals do wonderful things without any thinking on their part. Something inside prompts them. But usually these things have been done over and over through many generations of ancestors. Sometimes it's difficult to tell intelligence from instinct."

"Just what is instinct?" Sammy wanted to know.

"That's a tough one, Sammy," replied Tommy somewhat hesitatingly. "The dictionary says that instinct is 'natural and unreasoning prompting to action.' I memorized that." Tommy grinned.

"You didn't need to tell us," said Sammy dryly.

"The way I figure it," Tommy continued, "is that instinct is inherited knowledge of what to do under certain conditions that have been met often in the past, and that experience has taught how to meet."

"Listen to the professor!" jeered Sammy.

"When wholly new conditions arise, instinct falls down on the job and reason takes over," Tommy continued. "Young birds who have never seen a nest built go ahead and build the same kind of nest as their parents. That is done by instinct. Striped Chipmunk stores away food for winter, and this is done by instinct. But all the same, Striped Chipmunk has brains and uses them. I think this is true of most wild things just as it is with cats and dogs."

"But you can't prove that Striped Chipmunk does anything except by instinct," said Sammy.

"I think I can," replied Tommy. "Anyway, we'll test him out."

At once the others were all curiosity. "What kind of test?" demanded Sammy.

"I'll put some peanuts where he can get them in only one way," replied Tommy, "and that way under conditions he never has met before and probably none of his ancestors ever met either. If he works out that one way to get those peanuts, will you agree that he has used reason, not instinct?"

Over at a feeding station Striped Chipmunk was in the habit of coming to every day, Tommy drove two small posts a short distance apart. Between these, and several feet above the ground, he stretched a cord. From this he suspended peanuts by means of strings of varying lengths. None of these peanuts could the chipmunk reach from the ground except by jumping higher than was thought possible.

From the porch the three conspirators watched. It didn't take the chipmunk long to discover the peanuts. He stood up to reach as high as he could. The nearest peanut was still well out of reach. Then he tried jumping up. Still he couldn't reach

[16]

the peanut. He tried and tried again. It seemed useless. Those peanuts were beyond his reach.

The little striped squirrel sat down and studied those nuts swinging at the ends of the strings. The one nearest was tantalizing. Once more he gathered himself together and made a mighty jump. It took him higher than ever before. He caught that peanut with both hands and held on. Then he pulled himself up and curled his body around until he was holding to the peanut with all four feet. It didn't take him a second to see what held the peanut. He bit off the string and dropped to the ground with his prize. This he carried off to his storehouse and in a couple of minutes was back. As before, he jumped, but the best he could do was to touch one of the peanuts. Those nuts were most provoking. They were just out of reach, yet so little that they seemed to be within reach.

Again he sat down and studied them. He couldn't get them from the ground. He was sure of that. He climbed to the top of one of the posts. He reached out and took hold of the cord stretched between the posts. Could he walk out on it? He crept out a little way. Yes, he could keep his balance even though the cord was so very small.

Now he was right above one of the peanuts. He

looked down at it. It was even farther from him than when he had looked up at it from the ground. Could he reach it if he hung to the cord by his heels? He turned so that he was sitting crosswise on the cord. How he could keep his balance was more than Sue, Sammy and Tommy could understand. Holding fast to the cord with his hind feet, the chipmunk let himself down until he was hanging head down, stretched to his full length. Even so the peanut was beyond his reach.

With one hand he took hold of the string. In a flash he had an idea. He pulled on the string. It lifted the peanut. He reached with his other paw and grabbed the string, then hand over hand, or paw over paw if you like, he pulled up that string until the peanut was within his reach. Then he pulled himself back up on the cord, bit the string off where it was tied to the peanut, carefully made his way back to the post, ran down this and scampered off with his prize.

Soon he was back. This time there was no hesitancy. He ran up a post and out along the cord. Paw over paw he pulled up another peanut.

"Instinct or intelligence?" asked Tommy as he tied some more peanuts to the cord.

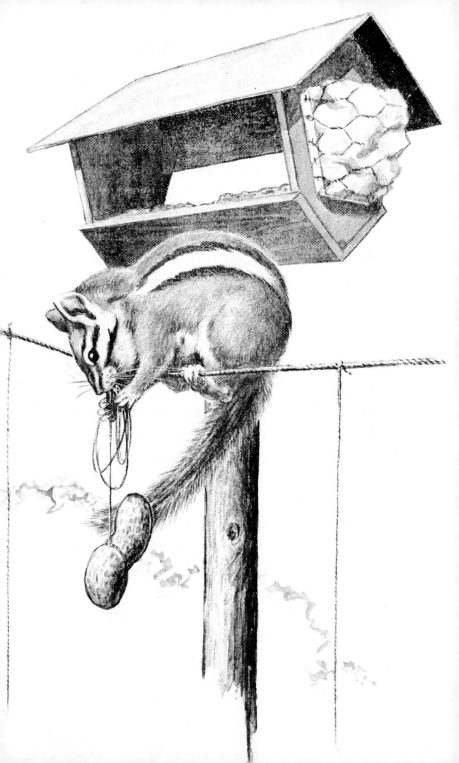

"He's smart," declared Sammy. "I wouldn't have believed it if I hadn't seen it."

"You could almost see him think when he was sitting under those nuts," said Sue.

"I wonder if he really did think, or if something inside prompted him to do what he did without any reasoning," said Tommy.

"Do you mean you wonder if he acted by instinct?" asked Sammy.

"I can see how it might be possible he did," replied Tommy. "When I planned this test I didn't see how instinct could possibly have anything to do with it, but now I'm not so sure."

"Well, I am," declared Sue. "Never before did he have to get anything that way, so how can you say that instinct had anything to do with it?"

Tommy laughed. "I didn't say that it had. I said that I could see that it might have had."

"Well, I can't," declared Sammy. "How do you get that way?"

"I happened to remember something," said Tommy.

"What did you happen to remember?" Sue wanted to know.

"I remembered seeing that chipmunk up in a maple tree this spring getting maple keys, the seeds you know. He would hang to a twig, reach down and pull up a bunch of keys from below. No doubt his ancestors did the same thing. When you come to think of it he used the same idea to get those peanuts," said Tommy.

"I don't care if he did. He thought that out. I know he did. You needn't try to tell me, Tommy Brown, that wasn't intelligence," declared Sue a bit indignantly, and Sammy nodded agreement.

"I like to think so myself," said Tommy, "because I believe that animals do reason. Just the same I can see why some people wouldn't think that was anything more than instinctive action. It's one of those cases where there's room for difference of opinion."

"I don't think so," asserted Sue.

3

Tommy's Insect Soup

The twins were on the back doorstep trying to decide what to do. Tommy came with a pail of milk from the barn. Helping with the milking was part of what he called his morning chores.

"Hi, Tommy! What are we going to do this morning?" demanded Sammy.

"How would you like to go over and meet Uncle Ben? He lives all by himself and he knows more about animals and birds and flowers and plants than anybody else. I've ever known. He's a regular old sport, and we all love him. So will you when you meet him," replied Tommy.

"I'd love to!" cried Sue, and Sammy agreed. So after Tommy had finished his morning work they started down across the meadow toward the home of Uncle Ben.

"Did you ever see a pitcher plant?" asked Tommy

as they stood at the edge of a wet place in the meadow.

"What's a pitcher plant?" Sue wanted to know.

"A plant with leaves like pitchers," replied Tommy.

"Not really!" cried Sue. "You needn't think, Tommy Brown, that because we come from the city you can tell us any old thing and we'll believe it. The idea of a plant with leaves like pitchers! Will they hold water?"

"Of course they'll hold water," retorted Tommy. "Come with me and I'll show you some. Probably you'll get your feet wet."

"I don't care, I'm wearing old sneakers. It won't matter how wet they get," replied Sue.

"Are there likely to be snakes there?" asked Sammy.

"There may be. What of it?" grinned Tommy.

"I don't like snakes," said Sammy.

"You mean, you're afraid of them," teased his cousin.

"I'll go with you!" Sue's black eyes sparkled. "Sammy can wait here. You just show me those pitcher plants. I don't believe there is such a thing."

"So of course you won't believe it when I tell you they eat insects," said Tommy.

"Do you mean the snakes?" asked Sue.

"No, the plants," retorted Tommy. He grinned in the most provoking way.

Sue tossed her head. Her black eyes fairly snapped. "Now I know you've made it all up, Tommy, but I'll go with you just the same. Who ever heard of plants eating insects? How do they get them to eat?"

"They catch them," said Tommy.

"How?" demanded Sammy, who had been listening.

"In their pitchers. Honest they do. That's what the pitchers are for. You needn't believe it, but that won't stop those plants from catching and eating insects," declared Tommy. He flashed a grin that was more provoking than ever.

"The idea! The very idea of plants eating insects!" Sue said over and over to herself. "Insects eat plants, but who ever heard of plants eating insects? I'll bet it's a joke of some kind. I have half a mind not to go."

But she did go and Sammy tagged along. They were so curious they just had to go. In a very damp place where there was a little standing water, Tommy stopped and pointed down to a queer-looking plant. It was very low-growing. The leaves spread out from a center, pointing in all directions like a rosette. They were the queerest-looking leaves Sue and Sammy had ever seen. Each was shaped like a pitcher without a handle, but instead of being bigger at the base, as a real pitcher is, they became smaller there to form a very short stem. Each had a sort of scalloped lip. Each was more than half filled with water.

"Now do you believe in pitcher plants?" cried Tommy triumphantly.

Sue admitted that she did, and that she could believe almost anything. "I think they're just too wonderful," said she. "Why do you suppose they grow that way, to hold all that water? What do they need it for?"

"To make soup. You can't make soup without water," chuckled Tommy.

Sue pouted. "Stop teasing us, Tommy Brown!" she cried. "Tell us what you mean."

Tommy picked one of the leaves and the twins drew close to look in it. "Do you see all those insects in it?" he asked.

"Of course we see them," replied Sue. "The poor things must have fallen in and drowned."

Tommy shook his head. "They didn't fall in," said he. "They went in of their own accord and then couldn't get out."

"What did they go in for?" demanded Sammy.

"For sweet juices or something of the kind down at the bottom," replied Tommy.

"There's one trying to get out now and can't."

"Why can't it?" demanded Sammy.

"Don't you see all those little hairs pointing down? The insects can't get up past them. Finally they give up and drown. See how the lower part where it's narrow is packed full of what is left of insects that have been caught. I guess the plant sort of drinks the water and lives on the insects that way. You can see for yourself that it's a sort of insect soup," explained Tommy.

"Doesn't the plant have roots and grow like other plants?" Sue wanted to know.

"Sure," replied Tommy. "I guess the insect soup is extra. We'll ask Uncle Ben when we get over there."

Sue made a face. "It's wonderful but I don't think I like it. Somehow it doesn't seem right for a plant to do anything like that," said she.

"There are other kinds of plants that catch insects," said Tommy. "There are other kinds of

pitcher plants in other parts of the country. I think perhaps Uncle Ben has some over at his place. He did have at one time. He sent away for them. Come on, let's go over and see him."

They found Uncle Ben in a spotlessly neat log cabin on the shore of a small pond from which a brook danced merrily over rocks for a little way, then stole off through a meadow. Uncle Ben was a small man with twinkling blue eyes and white hair. His laugh was a joy to hear. The twins liked him at once. Tommy told him about their visit to the pitcher plants.

"So then you brought them over here to see mine," laughed Uncle Ben.

He led them down near the edge of the pond and there, sure enough, were growing some pitcher plants. They were very different from the ones back in the meadow. These were more like vases than pitchers. They were of several sizes. Some were quite tall and these had raised lids over the tops, somewhat like the familiar jack-in-the-pulpit. Three different kinds were growing side by side.

"Do they like insect soup too?" Sammy asked.

Uncle Ben gave him a funny look. "What's this about insect soup?" he asked.

Sue giggled. "That's what Tommy calls the water full of drowned insects in those pitcher plants back there," said she.

Uncle Ben laughed. It was a laugh good to hear. "Insect soup is a new one to me," he said. "I hadn't thought of it in that term, but I guess that's about what it is. Yes, these plants live on it too. Just peek into them and you'll see for yourselves."

Sure enough, each of the slim, tall, vase-like plants was more than half filled with water and drowned insects.

"I wonder if it's the same kind of soup in each kind of plant," said Sammy, as he bent over to look into a couple growing side by side which were different from each other. He looked up with an odd expression. "It's different," said he.

"What do you mean it's different?" asked Tommy.

"There are two different kinds of insects, but the insects in each plant are all of one kind," explained Sammy.

Uncle Ben nodded. "One kind has been catching tiny bees. Another kind has been catching small flies, and still another has been catching little beetles. Apparently they have different tastes," said he and laughed. "These plants you see here came up from the sunny South. They wouldn't live through the winter outside here, but I kept some in my cabin all winter."

"I don't think I like them," said Sue. "I don't like to think of plants being eaters of living things."

"I don't see that it is any worse for plants to catch insects than for birds to do it," said Sammy.

"Oh, that's different," said Sue.

"Not so very different, my dear, when you come to think it over," said Uncle Ben.

4

Uncle Ben Goes Along

It was a bright summer morning, just the kind of morning to be out in the fields and woods. Tommy had had to go to the village. Sammy had borrowed his air gun and said he was going to hunt woodchucks. Of course Sue was going along. The twins were like that. They started down the road that led past Uncle Ben's cabin. He saw them coming and smiled because they looked so eager and happy.

"Well, well, well, well! Where are you going?" he asked as they joined him.

"Hunting," replied Sammy.

Uncle Ben raised his shaggy white eyebrows in pretended surprise. "This isn't the hunting season," said he.

"Oh yes, it is for woodchucks. I looked it up and they can be hunted anytime," said Sammy.

"Yesterday, when we were out with the dog, he

chased a chuck into a stone wall and we're going up there now to see if we can get a shot at him," said Sue.

"May I go too?" asked Uncle Ben. There was a twinkle in his blue eyes.

Sammy looked a little doubtful, but he couldn't very well refuse. So Uncle Ben joined them and they started up the road. Presently they came to an old pasture. There was an old stone wall along the side of the road. Sammy crept up to it and peeked over. Then he ducked down quickly. He turned and beckoned to Sue. He looked excited.

On hands and knees Sue crept over beside Sammy. "Raise up just enough to see over the wall," whispered Sammy. "Look out to that big rock in the middle of the pasture. In front of it is a pile of yellow sand. That's where that chuck's hole is. He's sitting there right now on that mound."

Slowly both raised up. Uncle Ben smiled as he watched them from the road. Sue was disappointed. All she saw was what looked like a short brown stake on the mound in front of the rock. "I don't see any woodchuck," said she, and raised up higher.

Instantly that stake kicked up a pair of black heels and dived out of sight behind the mound.

"Oh!" cried Sue and stood up.

"Now you've done it!" cried Sammy. He sounded disgusted and cross. He was both. "There's no use hunting here any more this morning. You've spoiled the fun. If you had kept down the way I did, he wouldn't have seen you," he scolded.

Just then Uncle Ben joined them. "He would have seen you long before you could have crept anywhere near him, Sammy," said he.

"I could have had the fun of trying," muttered Sammy.

"Even had you gotten near enough to shoot you couldn't have killed him with that air rifle. You might have hurt him, but that would have been all. Just why do you want to shoot him anyway?" said Uncle Ben.

"Oh, just for fun," replied Sammy.

"I don't see any fun in killing things," spoke up Sue.

"There isn't, my dear," said Uncle Ben. "It is a mistaken idea. The fun is in the hunting. The killing ends that. A dead chuck is no fun to anyone."

"Live woodchucks are no good. They're worse than no good. They eat up gardens. They make holes in pastures and meadows for cattle to step in. They ought to be killed," declared Sammy.

"How about this chuck here in this old pasture?

He isn't hurting anyone's garden. There are no cattle in the pasture to step in the holes he may make, so he's doing no harm to anybody. In fact, he's doing some good," said Uncle Ben.

It was clear that Sammy didn't believe that last statement. "What good?" he demanded.

"He is giving pleasure to others," was the quiet reply.

"Who?" asked Sammy. He looked puzzled and was.

"You," smiled Uncle Ben. "He's given you a little pleasant excitement every time you've seen him. You and Sue enjoyed hunting him this morning and the glimpse you had of him as you peeked over the old wall. This summer I've had a lot of fun coming up here early mornings to watch him and try to learn more about him. Yesterday an automobile stopped out there in the road and for some time the people in it sat looking over here. They were watching that chuck and enjoying it. One who gives pleasure to others certainly is doing good. That old chuck belongs here. Without him the old pasture would be a lonesome place. Woodchucks have no place in the garden, or a haying meadow, or a pasture where a horse or a cow may step in a hole and break a leg. From such places it is right and proper to remove them if need be. But on wasteland, and in such places as this, woodchucks rightfully belong. I love to hunt them there."

The twins stared hard at Uncle Ben. "I thought you didn't believe in hunting chucks," said Sue slowly, as if she were having hard work to believe she had heard aright.

"Oh, I do, my dear! Indeed I do — the right kind of hunting," was the prompt reply. The old man chuckled and somehow that chuckle was contagious. Sammy wanted to chuckle too, but he didn't know why.

"I hunt them to get better acquainted with them," continued Uncle Ben. "But I never hunt with a gun. Goodness, no! That isn't the way to get acquainted with anyone. That chuck over there is an old friend. I've known him for over four years."

"How do you know it's the same chuck? Tommy says there wasn't one there last summer, and Tommy knows," said Sammy.

Uncle Ben nodded. "That's right," said he. "There wasn't a chuck in this old pasture last year. He wasn't there until early this summer. A year ago he lived in the pasture on the other side of the road. The summer before that he was living near the edge of neighbor Wing's hayfield. I moved him from there."

"You moved him?" cried the two together.

The blue eyes twinkled as Uncle Ben looked at the two incredulous faces. "Yes," said he, "I moved him."

"How did you move him and what for?" cried Sue.

Uncle Ben smiled. "I caught him in a catch-him-alive-trap, which didn't hurt him in the least," said he. "I was afraid he'd get in trouble down in that mowing and get himself shot."

"Oh," said Sammy rather lamely.

"He's an interesting old fellow and I'm rather fond of him," said Uncle Ben.

At once Sammy wanted to know what was so interesting about a woodchuck. "All they do is eat and sit around," said he.

"How about the work they do? You know they dig underground homes, and it's quite a job," said Uncle Ben.

"They're stupid about that if you ask me," retorted Sammy. "They're stupid because they make a great pile of sand in front of the doorway and so advertise the location of their home. Anyone can find a woodchuck's hole."

"Which one?" asked Uncle Ben. There was a little smile on his face. Sue saw it.

"What do you mean by which one?" she asked.

"Usually a woodchuck has more than one door to his home," replied Uncle Ben. "True enough, the front door anyone can find. But Chucky doesn't mind that. It really doesn't count. It's the secret back door that counts. Sometimes he has more than one. Tommy would tell you that if he were here."

Sammy admitted that he had never heard of a chuck's back door and hadn't supposed he had one.

"So you had thought Chuck is stupid," continued Uncle Ben. "That's your mistake, laddie. A lot of other people have made the same mistake. A woodchuck is anything but stupid. To be safe from most enemies in summer, and from cold in winter, he has to dig his home deep in the ground below the line of frost. What else can he do with all that sand but pile it up at the entrance as a sort of doorstep? He certainly cannot carry it away. He knows as well as you do that it gives away the location of his home, really advertises it. He knows that with only one door an enemy who can dig would have him trapped. So he provides a way of escape, a back door, sometimes more than one. His main entrance is dug from the outside in. His back doors are dug from the inside out. All the sand is pushed back and out the front way. There is no telltale sand around the back doors, and they are used only in time of real need. Moreover, they are usually very well hidden."

"May we go over and see if we can find this chuck's back door?" Sue asked.

"Of course you may, my dear," replied Uncle Ben. "I hoped you would want to see that. This is the kind of hunting that I like."

Uncle Ben sat down on the big rock just back of the chuck's front door. The twins knelt to look down the hole, but they could see only a very little way. They then started to look for a back door. After a while Sammy called. His voice sounded doubtful. "I've found a hole, but I guess it's an old one," said he.

Sue hurried over to join him. The hole did look very much like an old, unused one. Grass grew to the very edge, and hung over the opening. One not looking for it might have stepped in it without seeing it. "That's one of Chuck's back doors," called Uncle Ben. "There are two more."

Sammy looked up quickly. "How do you know?" he called.

Uncle Ben laughed. It was a pleasant throaty little laugh. "Didn't I tell you this chuck and I are old, old friends?" he asked.

Just then there was a squeal from Sue, who had been prowling about. "Come here!" she cried. She had pulled aside some ferns that had grown in a clump quite a distance from the big rock. Right there in the middle was a hole. When she let go of the fern she was holding back, it fell over that hole and hid it completely. It didn't seem as if that hole could have any connection with any other, but Uncle Ben said it was another back door. The third was found beneath a prickly wild rose bush.

"What do you know about that? And you said a woodchuck is stupid!" cried Sue.

Sammy looked a little crestfallen. "He's smarter than I thought," he admitted.

"He's smarter than most people think, and a lot more interesting," declared Uncle Ben. "Imagine being able to sleep all winter without eating, or drinking, or feeling the cold. A woodchuck can do this and does. His cousin, the prairie dog, out in parts of the Great West does the same thing. So does another cousin who lives up in the mountains of the West and is called the whistler, or gray marmot. Woodchucks are marmots, you know. It's a sort of family name and they are what might be called second cousins to squirrels."

"I'm glad Sammy didn't shoot this old chuck. I'm coming over to visit him every day," declared Sue.

"I'll come with you and leave the gun behind. I guess there's a lot we don't know about him yet," said Sammy.

"A lot?" smiled Uncle Ben. "Probably you'll find out some things about him I don't know. But remember to keep out of his sight. He's bashful."

"We will," cried the twins. And Sue added, "I wish there were chucks in every old pasture. We could have a lot of fun watching them."

"Why not try hunting them with a camera?" suggested Uncle Ben. "I've made some very good shots with mine."

5

The Lovely Trap

"Uncle Ben, do you think animals do everything by instinct?" asked Sue.

"No," replied Uncle Ben, shaking his head. "No, I don't believe that at all. Some people do, but I don't. To believe that would be to deny intelligence, the ability to understand and reason. Many very wonderful things are done by instinct. In autumn and spring birds make long journeys, flying thousands of miles with no one to guide them. They do not get lost. Often they return to the very place from which they started. I would say that instinct, rather than intelligence, guides them. But when a friend's dog deliberately tried to outwit us, he was acting through intelligence, not instinct."

"What did he do?" Sammy wanted to know.

Uncle Ben laughed, and into his blue eyes came a faraway look. "His name was Bruce," said he. "He was a pointer, and like most hunting dogs was crazy to go afield. We boys often took Bruce with us, but there were times when we didn't want him. Always he was heartbroken when we left him behind.

"One day his master and I started for a walk and Bruce followed. He was sternly sent back, and with his tail between his legs he returned to the house and lay down on the porch. But when we were something like a mile from home I happened to look back, and there was Bruce just sneaking up behind us, his tail between his legs, and in his eyes a most beseeching look. It was too far to send him home and he knew it.

"Later a friend who had seen the whole thing told us all about it. Bruce had remained on the porch until we turned the first corner, then he ran to that corner and peeked around, showing no more than his nose and eyes. There he waited and watched until we turned the next corner, then repeated the performance. He did it a third time and then decided he could safely join us. Several times later on I saw the dog work that same trick. The rascal deliberately kept out of sight until he was sure he wouldn't be sent back. That was intelligence, not instinct."

"Is that a true story?" Sue wanted to know.

"Absolutely," Uncle Ben assured her.

Then the twins told him how Striped Chipmunk had solved the problem of getting the peanuts suspended beyond his reach. "Was that intelligence or was it instinct?" they asked.

"Tommy says it could have been instinct, but I think it was intelligence," declared Sue.

Tommy explained how he had seen squirrels in trees reach down and pull up buds or seeds from below, and how he had once seen a chipmunk do the same thing when gathering maple keys. "After all, pulling up those strings was much the same thing, it was the same idea," he concluded.

Uncle Ben agreed. "That's true," said he. "One of the most difficult things is to draw the line between instinct and intelligence. Perhaps that chipmunk used a little of both. Many very wonderful things that seem as if they must be the result of intelligent action are done wholly through instinct. Come with me and I'll show you a beautiful example of this."

He led the way to two trees standing some feet apart. Between them was a great web, a splendid example of the work of a spider belonging to the group known as the orb weavers. It was like a dainty piece of silvery lace. On a framework of

strong silken guidelines stretched between the trees had been woven the exquisite orb of the completed web. So perfectly was it woven, so securely anchored, it seemed that only intelligence of a high order could have produced it.

"Oh, what a lovely thing!" exclaimed Sue.

"It is so," replied Uncle Ben. "And," he added, "it's wholly the product of instinct. The spider that wove that web was little more than a living machine. If I should destroy that web probably she would weave another and do it automatically."

Sue was still full of questions. "Just what is instinct, anyway? Tommy says it is inherited knowledge of what to do under conditions that have been met with often in the past, and that experience has taught how to meet. He talks like a dictionary. I want to know what makes it work, if you know what I mean."

Fine little laugh lines were making wrinkles around Uncle Ben's eyes. He chuckled as he replied, "I know what you mean. If you should slip you would grab for the nearest thing within reach to keep you from falling and you would do it without thought, wouldn't you?" Sue nodded and Uncle Ben continued. "Your action would be instinctive, done without conscious thought, and the action of slipping would be the push button, so to speak, to cause the instinctive action to save yourself.

"Hunger prompts all creatures to look for food. Man is the only one who plans specific times for eating. Other living things do not think about eating until hunger prompts them instinctively to look for food. The desire for food prompted the maker of this web to weave it. Of course it's a trap, a lovely snare to catch food. Instinct, not reason, led to the spinning of the long guidelines, the framework. When this was finished the impulse to continue with those long straight lines of silk ceased. The completion of the framework gave the impulse that started the next operation, the bridging of the space between all those radiating lines with a series of threads so exactly spaced as to make the web. If I had cut some of those lines holding the framework, the spider couldn't have left off the bridgework she was doing to repair the break, because instinct works according to impulse and the impulse just then was for bridgework. Instinct is a sort of fixed force that is not to be diverted by the unusual, as reason would be. If the spider were working through intelligence, she would stop and repair the damage as soon as she discovered it, then return to what she had been doing. The impulse released by instinct just has to keep going until it has been used up. Anyway, that's how it looks to me. Do I sound like a dictionary too?"

"That's sort of deep, but I guess I get the idea," said Sammy. "You mean that instinct starts something and sees it through to a finish, no matter how foolish it may be."

"In many cases that is very true," replied Uncle Ben. "The spider that spun that silk and wove that web never had a spinning or weaving lesson in her life. When the time came for a web, instinct guided her step by step in what to do, and she did it like those automatic machines that today make so many various articles. She was just a sort of living machine herself while she was working. Intelligence, no matter how great it is, is likely to make mistakes. Instinct, if there is no outside interference, makes no mistakes. Instinct does marvelous things, but sometimes it does things that seem woefully stupid under changed or new conditions."

6

Sue's Change of Mind

Tommy and Sammy sat on the garden fence. They were waiting for Sue. "It's just like a girl not to be ready, or to have to go back for something," grumbled Sammy.

Just then there was a scream from the other side of the garden. "Oh, oh! The horrid thing!"

"Now what's she found? Probably a bug of some kind," said her brother disgustedly.

"Perhaps it's a snake," said Tommy mischievously. "Come on. Let's go see."

"What's the use of both of us going for just a bug or something? You go and I'll wait right here," said Sammy.

"So — o — o — " said Tommy softly. "You're afraid of a snake, aren't you?"

"Snakes are poisonous," said Sammy. "They can kill you!"

"There's none of that kind around here," said Tommy. "There are only four kinds of poisonous snakes in all North America, the rattlesnake and the copperhead in some parts of the North, and the cottonmouth moccasin and the coral in the South. All right, Mr. 'Fraidy, you stay here. Don't ever again make fun of Sue for being afraid of something."

Tommy started across the garden. Sammy, a little red in the face, followed. "What is it, Sue? What have you found?" asked Tommy as he drew near.

"It's a big, horrid old hoppy-toad, and I almost stepped on it. Ugh!" replied Sue in a tone of disgust.

"Pooh! 'Fraid of nothing but an old hoppy-toad!" exclaimed Sammy scornfully.

"Who is no more harmless than little Mr. Garter Snake and most of his cousins," added Tommy softly.

"There's something the matter with him," said Sue. She meant Old Mr. Toad. "Look at him! He's all swelled up! Toads are horrid things, all warty and everything."

"Old Mr. Toad is one of my good friends," said her cousin quietly.

"Tommy Brown, do you really mean to say you *like* him?" Sue cried incredulously.

"We usually like our friends, don't we?" replied Tommy. "Old Mr. Toad is one of my oldest and very best friends. The trouble with you, Sue, is that you haven't made his acquaintance yet."

Sue sniffed. "I'm acquainted with him all I want to be," said she. "Just see the horrid thing squirm! I wonder what's the matter with him."

"Come on!" cried Sammy. "There's nothing interesting about an old toad. Let's get going."

Tommy shook his head. "We'll stay right here," said he, "and Old Mr. Toad will make you swallow your words with his skin."

The twins stared at Tommy to see if he were joking. "What do you mean?" cried Sue. "I still think he's a horrid thing, and I wouldn't touch him for the world!"

Tommy chuckled. "Why not?" he asked.

"He'd give me warts," declared Sue promptly.

"He wouldn't do anything of the kind," retorted Tommy indignantly. "He wouldn't if he could. What's more, he couldn't if he would. The idea that he can give anybody warts is all hooey."

"Just the same, I think he's horrid," retorted

Sue. "Look at him now. What's the matter with him? He must be sick. What's he trying to do?"

Tommy laughed aloud. "He's just changing his suit," said he.

"Aw, go on!" said Sammy in a tone of disgust. "In the first place he doesn't wear a suit. He hasn't fur, or feathers, or even scales."

"I don't blame you a bit for thinking I'm trying to fool you," said Tommy. "I'm not. On my word, I'm not. Old Mr. Toad really is changing his suit, which happens to be his skin. You see, under his old suit he has a new suit, a new skin. He is one of the luckiest people I know, for every year he gets four new suits. That's more than most of us get. What's more, he doesn't have to worry where they're coming from."

Suddenly Sue cried out. "Oh! Oh! Oh! The poor thing!" she cried. "Just see what he's done. He's split his skin right down the middle of his back. He must have swelled up so much his skin burst. The poor thing! What are you laughing at, Tommy? I don't see anything to laugh at. How would you like to burst your skin?"

"I wouldn't like it," confessed Tommy. "But it's different with a toad. He wouldn't like it if he couldn't burst it. That split skin is really his old suit. Watch him now and you'll see him take it off. Of course it isn't considered polite to watch anyone change his clothes, but Old Mr. Toad won't mind. See, his pants have split down each leg."

"What makes him keep opening and closing his big mouth, and sort of swelling up?" Sammy asked.

"It's to help loosen that old skin. I've seen him do it before. See, he has his hind legs free now. It won't take more than five minutes to get that whole suit off," said Tommy.

Sue and Sammy squatted down on either side of Old Mr. Toad. Suddenly Sue fairly shrieked with delight. "Look! Look!" she cried. "He's trying to pull his suit off over his head the way Sammy pulls his sweater off. Oh, you funny thing!"

Tommy's eyes twinkled. "Have you noticed what he's doing with his old suit?" he asked.

"Why — why — why — he's swallowing it!" cried Sue excitedly.

"Oh rats! Who ever heard of anyone swallowing his suit, his own skin?" scoffed Sammy.

"He is too swallowing it! Isn't he, Tommy?" insisted Sue.

"He certainly is," replied her cousin.

Sue made a face at Sammy. "So there, Mr. Smarty," said she. "I guess I know what I see with

my own eyes. I wouldn't have missed this for anything."

"You seem to have changed your mind about
Old Mr. Toad," teased Tommy. "I thought you
would. You'll change it still more before we leave."

"Look!" cried Sue. "He's stuffing it in at one corner of his big mouth with his hand!"

"That's right, Sue. He sure is funny. See him
gulp and blink! Guess his old suit goes down rather
hard. I'm glad I don't have to get rid of my old
clothes that way," said Sammy.

"Now he's stuffing it in at the other corner of his
mouth with the other hand!" cried Sue delightedly.
"Oh my goodness, he's using both hands!"

"See him try to get his arms out of his sleeves.
There comes one!" exclaimed Sammy.

"It shows the shape of his whole hand like a tiny
glove wrong side out," giggled Sue.

"Now he's trying to get the other hand out. Here
it comes! I never saw anything funnier in all my
life. He's swallowed all but that one sleeve hanging
from the corner of his mouth. I wonder if it's because he hasn't room for that," said Sammy.

"And you're the one who declared there's nothing interesting about toads," teased his cousin.

"I take it all back. I'll swallow my words just as

you said I would. A fellow has to see some things to believe them," said Sammy.

"True, but don't believe everything you see, or think you see," warned Tommy. "Eyes are not always to be trusted."

"Speaking of eyes, see how bright Old Mr. Toad's are now," broke in Sue. Then she added in a tone of great surprise, "Why, he has golden eyes, and they're beautiful! I do believe they're the most beautiful eyes I've ever seen."

Tommy laughed. "I guess you're stretching that a little, Sue, but they are beautiful," said he. "Some great writer once mentioned the jewel in a toad's head. I guess he had discovered how lovely the eyes of a toad are. You should hear his love song in the spring. That's as sweet as his eyes are lovely."

Sammy looked at his cousin suspiciously. "Say, do you mean that or are you kidding us?" he drawled.

"Of course I mean it. If any kidding is being done it will be by you kidding yourself," retorted Tommy indignantly.

"Why doesn't he sing now?" demanded Sue.

"Because this is the wrong season of the year. When he was over in the pool you would have heard him. When he leaves the water he stops singing," explained Tommy.

"Wait a minute. Are you telling us that toad was way down in the Smiling Pool and came back all this distance?" exclaimed Sammy.

"Sure," replied Tommy. "That's the nearest water, and in the spring all mature toads go to the water for breeding. Come on now, let's be on our way."

"I wish we could take Old Mr. Toad with us," said Sue wistfully.

"What? That horrid thing?" teased her brother.

"He isn't horrid. He's a darling and I love him. So there!" declared Sue, stamping a foot indignantly.

7

Tommy Bluffs a Bluffer

The three cousins had crossed the garden and were climbing over the fence on the other side. They were still talking about toads. "The way I figure it," said Tommy, "is that the more toads I have in my garden the better garden I'll have. They live on all sorts of garden pests, and do no harm at all themselves. Listen! What was that?"

There it was again, a faint scream. It seemed to come from back where they had been watching Old Mr. Toad change his suit. It was faint but unmistakably a scream of fright. It was the scream of a small person in great fear. Tommy jumped from the fence and ran back. The others followed.

"I think something's happened to Old Mr. Toad," Tommy called back over his shoulder.

"We haven't been gone more than two minutes.

How could anything have happened to him in so short a time?" cried Sue.

Just then they saw Old Mr. Toad. He was struggling in the grip of the enemy he feared most. Sue shrieked and beat a hasty retreat. Sammy backed away in such a hurry that he tripped and sat down with a thump. He scrambled to his feet and began looking for a stick or a stone. A hog-nosed snake held Old Mr. Toad fast by one leg, which he already had well down his throat. Just as Old Mr. Toad had swallowed his old suit, a little at a time, so this ugly-looking snake had begun to swallow Old Mr. Toad. He didn't have a chance to do any more swallowing, for Tommy put a foot on the snake's neck. That made him promptly release Old Mr. Toad.

Poor Old Mr. Toad! Those beautiful eyes of his looked as if they would pop right out of his head. They were as golden as ever but their beauty was lost in a look of terror. He didn't stop to say thank you. He left in a hurry, with long jumps that would have been a credit to his cousin, Grandfather Frog.

Sammy came running up with a big stick which he held out to Tommy. "Here," he panted, going no nearer than necessary.

"What's that for, Sammy?" asked Tommy.

"To kill that old snake with," replied Sammy.

"I don't want to kill him," said Tommy.

"Why not?" cried Sammy and Sue together.

"Why should I?" asked Tommy.

"Because he's a snake and all snakes should be killed!" declared Sammy.

"That shows how much you know about snakes," retorted Tommy. "Most snakes do more good than harm. This fellow is one of the most harmless of the lot."

"I don't believe it! He's poisonous! Anyone would know that just to look at him!" retorted Sammy.

"There isn't a drop of poison in him," declared Tommy. "Just remember what I said a little while ago about not believing everything you see, or think you see. This fellow may look dangerous. I'll agree to that. But he isn't dangerous to anyone but Old Mr. Toad, or other small folk like him. He's a bluffer and nothing worse. I'll prove it to you."

Tommy kept his foot on the neck of the snake, despite the squirming and the struggling, until he could be sure that Old Mr. Toad had made his escape.

"Oh the poor thing!" cried Sue, looking on from a safe distance. "You said you didn't want him killed, yet see how you've flattened his head and neck! I think you're as mean as you can be, Tommy Brown. I think you're cruel. So there!"

Tommy smiled more broadly than ever. "A little while ago you thought Mr. Toad was horrid. Then you changed your mind and called him a darling because you found out that things are not always what they seem. Perhaps when you learn the truth about this old rascal here you'll change your mind about me. I haven't hurt him the least bit. I didn't flatten out his neck, he did that himself. It's a great help to him in doing his specialty."

"Specialty! What is his specialty?" asked Sammy, who had been keeping as far away as his sister.

"Looking ugly. Looking dangerous so as to scare people like you, and make them afraid," said Tommy. "The first time I met him he scared me so that for a week afterward I wouldn't go near the place where I had seen him. I didn't know him then. Now I do, and he can't bluff me any more. If he didn't flatten his neck that way he wouldn't look half so ugly. He's just pretending to be a bad one when all the time he's nothing of the kind. Watch him now."

Old Mr. Toad was making good his escape, so

Tommy lifed his foot and stepped aside. At once the snake partly coiled and in the middle of the coil the end of his tail lifted and vibrated, much as a rattlesnake's does when he is shaking his rattles. With a stick Tommy poked him and the hiss that followed made the twins jump. It sounded like hot iron thrust into water. Tommy reached down.

"Watch out, Tommy!" shrieked Sue as the snake struck at Tommy's hand. "Oh Tommy, did he bite you?"

Tommy laughed and held out his hand. "Do you see any marks?" he asked. Then he added, "His mouth was closed. He just hit at my hand with his nose. Like the flattening of his neck and his hissing, that was just a bluff."

Sammy, afraid but rather ashamed of his fear, had drawn nearer. "If all this is a bluff, he's some actor," said he.

Tommy laughed. "You haven't seen anything yet," said he as he picked up a stick. "Now you'll see some honest to goodness acting, unless the old rascal remembers that I can't be fooled. This is not the first time I've rescued Old Mr. Toad. Now watch."

With the stick Tommy began to beat the ground, first on one side of Bluffer, then on the other side and close to him. Bluffer hissed and struck savagely. This continued for a few minutes. Then abruptly the snake began to writhe about on the ground, twisting and turning as if in great pain. Finally he seemed to go into convulsions. This was too much for Sue's tender heart.

"Stop it!" she cried, stamping a foot. "Stop it, you cruel thing!"

Just then the snake rolled over on its back, the convulsions ceased, the mouth was opened and the slender forked tongue hung out. To all appearances, Bluffer was a dead snake.

"There now, you've killed him!" cried Sue. "You didn't have to do that. I think it's dreadful, Tommy Brown!"

Tommy showed no signs of regret. He even chuckled as he picked the snake up by the tail. The snake hung limp and seemingly lifeless. "Didn't I tell you his name is Bluffer? He's just proving true to his name," said he and held out the snake.

"You needn't pretend that he isn't dead," scolded Sue. "You may not have intended to hit him but you must have. I didn't like him. I was afraid of him. But I didn't want him killed."

"Do you see any mark on him where he was hit? You don't, because I didn't hit him. Look at his neck. You accused me of flattening it when I put my foot on him, but it isn't flat now."

True enough, that neck was no longer flattened. Somehow Bluffer didn't look nearly so ugly or dangerous.

"See how his nose turns up like the nose of a hog?" said Tommy. "That's why he's called the hog-nosed snake. Because of the way he hisses some folks call him a puff adder and some call him a blow adder. I like my name for him better, Bluffer."

"Now that you've killed him, what are you going to do with him?" Sammy wanted to know.

Tommy's eyes twinkled. "Take him where, when he comes to life again, he won't find Old Mr. Toad. Then I'll let him go," said Tommy.

"Look here, do you really expect us to believe that snake isn't dead?" Sammy spoke a bit sharply. "Quit your fooling," he added.

"There isn't a thing the matter with him. Follow me and I'll prove it to you," declared Tommy. Still carrying the snake by the tail, he started off. He led the way across the garden over to the edge of the woods. There he stopped. He held the snake out toward Sue. "Don't you want to hold him?" he asked mischievously.

Hastily Sue backed up a few steps and put her

hands behind her. "I wouldn't touch the cold clammy thing for the world!" she exclaimed.

"There's where you are wrong again," declared Tommy. "Snakes are not cold and clammy. If you touch him on the back you will find it almost velvety. I dare you to touch him, Sue."

Sue looked up at her brother and her reply was wholly unexpected. "I will if Sammy will," she declared.

"Aw, I don't want to," said Sammy with a sickly sort of grin.

"You dassent. You know you dassent," said Sue.

"Come on, Sammy. Don't let a girl dare you. A dead snake can't hurt you," said Tommy, holding the snake toward him.

Hesitatingly, Sammy extended an exploring finger. "Why — why — why, it isn't at all as I thought," he admitted. "I wish you hadn't killed him."

"So you still don't believe me when I say that I haven't hurt him the least bit! All right, now watch me bring him to life," replied Tommy.

Stooping, he gently placed Bluffer on the ground on his belly. Instantly the snake rolled over on his back and was as lifeless as before. Tommy rolled him over on his belly. The snake promptly turned on his back. "He seems to think that to be properly dead he must be on his back," chuckled Tommy. "Now we'll go off a little way and watch."

They walked off where Bluffer couldn't see them, but they could see him. When all was quiet, the snake slowly rolled over. Very cautiously he lifted his head to look unwinkingly this way and that. His quivering tongue darted out. Then he began to move away through the grass. Tommy looked at his cousins. Their faces were a study.

"I like him!" declared Sue unexpectedly. "He's funny. He's a perfect actor. Make him do it again, Tommy."

Tommy shook his head. "He wouldn't do it again now," said he. "He isn't stupid, that fellow. He didn't go through that performance to amuse us but to fool us, to bluff us. Having failed, he won't try it again right away. We won't bother him any more. I just wanted you two to know how harmless he is to man, even though he looks so ugly. It's too bad that so many folk are afraid of all snakes and want to kill every one they see. They're wonderful, snakes are."

"I don't see anything wonderful about them," sniffed Sammy.

"I do," cried Sue. "Without legs or feet they run fast. I never thought of that before."

"And some are good climbers, and others without fins are good swimmers," Tommy added.

"And they can't blink because they haven't any eyelids. They haven't any ears, so they find out things with their tongues. Truly they are wonderful!" cried Sue.

"Don't forget the actor," said Tommy.

Sammy grinned. "Some actor — wonderful!" he agreed.

8

Mrs. Snapper Has Important Business

The two boys were off on a fishing trip, and Sue was left to her own devices. It was a lovely morning and she decided to go over to the Smiling Pool. Tommy had told her of a fish in there that did funny things. Anyway, to her they seemed funny things for a fish to do. "Tommy says it's all true, so I suppose it is. But it would be a lot easier to believe if I could see it with my own eyes," she thought as she walked across the meadows.

Bubbling Bob the Bobolink, in his handsome coat of black and white with buff trimmings, was pouring out in song the joy in his heart, as only he could. From out in the middle of the meadow came the clear, equally joyous notes of Carol the Meadowlark. Sue knew that somewhere on the ground,

hidden in the grass, were two nests. In vain she had looked for them. Undoubtedly in one Mrs. Bobolink was sitting on her eggs and listening to the bubbling song of her handsome mate, not in the least jealous because he was so finely dressed while she wore a coat of modest brown. Equally well-hidden Mrs. Meadowlark was doing the same thing in equal contentment, listening to Carol's clear, lilting notes, knowing that they were intended just for her.

"Perhaps it is just as well I haven't found those nests," thought Sue as she stopped to listen. "Had I found them the birds would be worried, perhaps too worried to sing. Then the morning wouldn't be quite so beautiful as it now is. It seems as if there is beauty everywhere. Oh–h! Oh–h!"

There were startled surprise and fright in that

shriek. A sharp, unpleasant hiss had stopped her abruptly and brought her attention to the ground just in front of her. There was no beauty in what she saw almost at her feet. On the contrary it was, as she afterward described it, the ugliest-looking thing she had ever seen. It was no wonder she had shrieked, and it was no wonder that now at a second threatening hiss she jumped back. A very big snapping turtle was facing her. It was plain to see that this meeting was no more to the liking of Mrs. Snapper than it was to Sue.

"You awful thing!" cried Sue. She hastily backed away a few steps. "What are you doing over here? Go back to the water where you belong!" Sue stamped her foot and that drew another angry hiss. It was unpleasantly clear that Mrs. Snapper was not afraid, and that she had no intention of going back.

The big turtle was not pretty to look at. She was bigger than Sue had dreamed a freshwater turtle could ever be. To the startled girl she probably looked much bigger than she really was. She wasn't as big around as an old-fashioned washtub, as Sue described her when first telling of the incident, but she was plenty big. She wasn't round, since her shell was longer than it was broad. It was the first time

Sue had seen a snapping turtle out of water and close to. She had seen Mrs. Snapper's head above water out in the Smiling Pool and it had looked comparatively small. She hadn't dreamed that it was as big as it now appeared to be. With its stout, hooked, beak-like jaws and rather small beady eyes, it was wicked-looking. Yes, sir, it was wicked-looking. The snake-like neck, so long that it could not be drawn back into the shell as can be done by so many other turtles, added nothing of beauty. Mrs. Snapper had spent so much time in the mud at the bottom of the Smiling Pool that tiny water plants called algae were growing on her shell, giving it a slight greenish shade. For a turtle, she had quite a long tail. It bore a crest of horny points.

Mrs. Snapper lost her temper. She was in the habit of losing it easily. It is a family trait. She began to move forward in a most determined way. There was no sign of fear. Sue stepped aside and Mrs. Snapper paid no more attention to her. "It acts as if it's going somewhere for a purpose and knows exactly where," said Sue to herself.

Snapper and Mrs. Snapper were old-timers in the Smiling Pool. They had lived there for many years. They knew every inch of the muddy bottom. They knew every stick and stone along the banks.

They had no friends among the other folk in the pool. They were disliked by all, and by some they were both feared and hated. They spent most of their time doing nothing. Anyway, that's how it seemed. The fact is they were lying in wait for the unsuspecting and the careless. They did little honest hunting for their food. Now and then an innocent duckling would swim overhead. Snapper or Mrs. Snapper would soundlessly rise beneath the young swimmer and it would never be seen again. It was easy to lie half-buried in the mud and wait for a dinner to swim unsuspectingly within reach.

Now there comes a time every year when Mrs. Snapper must go ashore. She has important business that requires a journey on land. She must find a place to lay her eggs. Left in the water, they would not hatch. They must be buried on land in warm earth. She, who spends practically all her life in water, must lay her eggs on land, just as Mrs. Toad, who spends most of her life on land, must seek the water in which to lay her eggs. Sometimes it does seem to be a topsy-turvy world we live in.

Of all this Sue knew nothing. The morning she had started to visit the Smiling Pool was the very morning that Mrs. Snapper had chosen for her annual trip ashore. Now Sue was a little in doubt.

Should she or should she not follow Mrs. Snapper? Finally, curiosity overcame timidity and she followed at a safe distance.

"I haven't the least idea where that turtle is going, but it certainly is on its way somewhere. I'd hate to have to try stopping the hateful thing. It looks as if it could bite a nail in two. It looks positively dangerous," thought Sue. She didn't know then if this was Snapper or Mrs. Snapper.

The big turtle forced her way through the grass, leaving it flattened in a little path behind her. It was hard going, but she persisted. Presently she came to a piece of newly plowed land. Along one of the furrows she made her way with some difficulty. Two or three times she stopped for a moment to scratch the side of the furrow, then went on. She climbed over into the next furrow and pushed her way along this. At last she stopped. She seemed to fuss around a bit. Then she began to dig in the soft earth.

Sue moved near enough for a good view. "For the land's sake!" she exclaimed under her breath. "That critter is digging a hole with its hind feet and at the same time backing into it. Is it trying to bury itself?"

Mrs. Snapper kept on digging and sinking into

the ground. The loose earth fell back around her. When she was nearly covered, she stopped digging.

"The poor thing is all tired out and is resting. I won't bother it. I'll just wait until it moves on," said Sue to herself.

But Mrs. Snapper didn't move on, and Sue was short on patience. It was too lovely a morning to waste watching an ugly old turtle.

When the boys returned for lunch Sue had a question for Tommy. "Do turtles often come out on land? I saw the biggest, ugliest old turtle way up on the meadow this morning."

"There are some land turtles, but water turtles don't come out on land much. They sometimes climb out on old logs or floating stuff for a sunbath. They always stay where they can easily slide into the water," said Tommy.

"This one didn't. It was such a big, ugly-looking thing that it scared me. It hissed at me. It was a long way from the Smiling Pool and going still farther away," declared Sue.

Now she had Tommy's full attention. He had Sue describe the turtle and the place where she had met it. "That was Mrs. Snapper," he declared. "She was on her way to find a place to lay her eggs. I wish I had been there. She and Snapper have cost me plenty, taking my young ducks. I have known one of them to pull down a fully grown duck. I don't suppose you know where she finally went."

"I know where she stopped to rest. I left her half-buried in the ground," replied Sue.

"Where?" cried Tommy. He looked and sounded excited.

"In that place where you and Uncle have been plowing," explained Sue. "The poor thing got tired out trying to walk in those furrows."

"Tired out, my eye!" exclaimed her cousin inelegantly. "She was there to lay her eggs, and she was doing just that when you thought she was resting. Do you think you could find the exact spot again, Sue?"

"I don't know. I guess I could. Why do you want to know, Tommy?" inquired Sue.

"So I can get those eggs," was the prompt response. "There may be two dozen of them. I don't like to think of a lot more snapping turtles in the Smiling Pool. This afternoon we'll see if we can find those eggs."

A heavy thundershower made it late afternoon before the three egg hunters got over to the plowed field. Now the furrows of a newly plowed field look very much alike. Sue hadn't paid close attention to which furrow Mrs. Snapper had been in. Then, too, the shower had washed away all traces Mrs. Snapper had left. There was nothing to show that she had been there. Those eggs were laid and buried, and the mother was back in the Smiling Pool and glad to be there.

"When you thought Mrs. Snapper was resting, Sue, she was laying her eggs," explained Tommy again. "When she was through she just crawled out of the hole and the loose earth slid off her shell and covered her eggs. Maybe she smoothed the place over a little. I don't know about that. Then along came that heavy shower and washed away all signs. I bet she couldn't find those eggs now herself if she wanted to."

"When will they hatch?" Sammy wanted to know.

"Not until September, if they do hatch," replied Tommy.

"What do you mean, Tommy, by saying 'if they do hatch'?" cried Sue.

"This is the last of June. A lot of things can happen between now and September. I might even find those eggs myself. Then they certainly wouldn't hatch," replied Tommy with a grin.

"Think of that poor mother turtle doing all that

work of burying those eggs and you say you wouldn't let them hatch," said Sue.

Tommy chuckled. "Forget that mother business and don't get sentimental, Sue. By this time Mrs. Snapper has forgotten those eggs. She never would know anyway whether they hatched or not. She wouldn't know her own children if she should meet them. The babies hatch out in the ground, dig their way out, and head for the nearest water. Pa and Ma mean nothing at all to a baby turtle. Forget it, Sue, and save your pity," said he.

"I think those eggs are more seeds than eggs. That turtle planted them. Whoever heard of planting eggs?" said Sammy.

"Stick around awhile longer, wise guy, and you'll learn a lot you never heard of," retorted Tommy pleasantly.

9

Fishy but True

In the excitement of the turtle and her eggs Sue had forgotten the funny fish she had started out to look for. She remembered this the next day and begged Tommy to show her the fish. On the way to the Smiling Pool they skirted the piece of plowed ground. Tommy walked in one of the furrows. Off to one side in another furrow he spotted a place where someone had been digging. He went over to it. There was a shallow but quite large hole, as if someone had tried to make sure of all that might have been hidden there. He called the others over. "The place of the buried treasure has been found," said he. Thrown aside in the earth was a small white scrap. He picked it up and held it out for the others to see. "Shell," said he. "Turtle egg shell. Someone has had a feast and that someone was Jimmy Skunk."

"How do you know?" cried Sammy. "I bet you're just guessing."

"Use your eyes, boy," retorted his cousin. "There are the prints of his hind feet. And here are some good prints of his front feet. Well, well, well, what do you know about this?" He pointed to another print in the soft earth.

"Well, what about it?" demanded Sammy.

Tommy didn't reply at once. He bent over, studying the ground as he slowly moved this way and that. He was taking pains not to step where any prints were visible. Finally he looked up at his two cousins, and his freckled face wore a wise smile. "I wish I had been here last night," said he.

"Why?" chorused the two.

"To see who got the most eggs. Bobby Coon found them first," replied Tommy.

Sammy gave his cousin a skeptical look. "Can you prove that?" he asked.

Tommy pointed to a footprint that clearly was different from the skunk print. "That is a footprint of a raccoon," said he. "Crossing it is a skunk's footprint. So of course the coon was here first. He found those eggs and dug them out. The skunk happened along and demanded his share. Right here you can see where the skunk stamped with his front feet. Over there you can see where the coon jumped back in a hurry. My guess is that each had a good share of eggs. Anyway, there will be no baby snappers in the Smiling Pool next year to grow up and make trouble."

The three went on their way and soon were seated comfortably on the high bank of the Smiling Pool. Over near the opposite shore, the top of a pile of dead brown rushes showed above the surface of the water. It was like a small edition of a beaver lodge. It was a muskrat house. A brown head appeared from among some growing rushes and moved toward that house in the water.

"Jerry Muskrat!" cried Sue and pointed.

There was a splash, the brown head disappeared, and only widening circles on the water showed he had been there. A few minutes later Sue's attention was caught by a small fish swimming close inshore right below them.

"Look at that funny little fish! It's shaped like a pumpkin seed!" cried Sue.

Tommy laughed. "That's just what it is called — pumpkin seed. It's also called sunfish. It's one of the funny little fishes I wanted you to see. When the sun strikes Mr. Sunfish just right he shows as pretty colors as any fish I know of. He's as spunky

as he is pretty. Look at his big eyes and see how he uses them. No one is going to pull a surprise party if he can help it, and usually he can. You should see him in the spring."

"Why then any more than now?" Sue wanted to know.

"To begin with he's prettier, his colors are brighter. He's even more scrappy then than now and — " Tommy paused.

"And what?" demanded Sammy.

"He's one of the busiest folk in the Smiling Pool," Tommy finished.

"Doing what?" asked Sammy.

"Preparing a place for Mrs. Pumpkin Seed to lay her eggs, then keeping guard over those eggs until they hatch and the babies leave home," explained Tommy. "You should see him clean off a place on the bottom for those eggs. You really should. He even picks up tiny pebbles in his mouth and takes them off to one side. And is he thorough! When Mrs. Pumpkin Seed has deposited her eggs on that nice clean place he made for them, he takes over and she goes off to do what she pleases. Her duty is done, but not his. He is on the job every minute, driving off any other fish or intruder that may threaten those precious eggs. When the eggs hatch he turns nurse and protector until the young leave him and scatter. He's a good father, that spunky little scrapper."

Sue looked down with new interest at the little finny warrior. "You funny little fish," said she. "And I didn't think there was anything interesting about fish except the fun of catching them."

"Look!" exclaimed Tommy. "There's a bullhead."

Sure enough, a bullhead or horned pout, a small member of the catfish family, had just swum into view.

Sue made a face. "I think he's horrid! Anyway, he's horrid-looking," she declared.

Tommy laughed. "I guess maybe you're right, Sue," said he. "He may not be exactly horridlooking, but he certainly is homely and not pleasing to look at. However, he has his good points. Yes, sir, Bullhead has his good points."

Sammy fairly snorted. "He has his points all right!" he exclaimed and grinned a bit ruefully when they laughed at him. He was still nursing a sore hand, the result of ignorance and excitement on a recent fishing trip when he had grabbed up a lively bullhead he had just pulled from the water and so had discovered the so-called horns, the sharp spine that is always ready to avenge rough handling by the unwary.

"You don't call that a good point and I don't blame you. Just the same, he does have some good points," said Tommy.

"Such as, for instance?" cried Sammy.

"He is good to eat," replied Tommy.

Sue giggled. "Sammy thought so the other night when we had those bullheads for dinner," said she.

"I'll admit that," agreed Sammy. "That's point one. You said points."

"Mr. and Mrs. Bullhead are good parents," declared Tommy.

"Don't make me laugh," retorted Sammy. "Fish don't even know when they are parents. They just lay their eggs and go off and forget them." Then he remembered the little sunfish and added hastily, "That is, most fish."

"That is probably true of most fish, but it isn't true of the bullhead," declared Tommy.

"Are you telling us that those ugly mud-lovers care for anything but mud and enough to eat?" demanded Sammy.

Tommy nodded. "Something like that. I agree that Mr. and Mrs. Bullhead are ugly-looking, that they like to poke about in the mud and that there's nothing pleasant about them but their flesh when cooked," said Tommy. "But just the same, they are good parents. What is more, they work together in preparing a place for the eggs and, after the eggs hatch, in taking care of the young. I know because I've watched them."

"Watched them do what?" Sue wanted to know.

"Watched them prepare the nest for one thing. If you were here in the spring you could watch them too. I wish you could do that," said their cousin.

"We wish we could too, don't we, Sammy? Tell us about it," begged Sue.

"Well, first they look the bottom of the pool all over. Anyway, I think they do, for at that season of the year I've seen them swimming in all parts of the pool," said Tommy. "Finally they choose a place where the water is shallow and the bottom is gravelly or sandy. Usually it is under something, perhaps an old log. They make a little saucer-shaped place by taking away all the pebbles, coarse gravel and loose stuff. They suck it into their big mouths and carry it off. When they have a nice clean sandy nest, Mrs. Bullhead deposits her eggs and Pa goes on guard, the same way Pumpkin Seed watches over his eggs. Bullhead is right on the job every minute."

Sammy looked down at the fish with new interest. "He doesn't look it," he declared. "That is, he doesn't look as if he had that much intelligence, as if he would know enough to do such things, or would have any family feeling one way or the other."

"You never can tell just by looks," said Sue.

"I'll say you can't," agreed Sammy.

"It is said that when the eggs hatch both the father and mother watch over the babies," continued Tommy. "As soon as the babies are big enough they are led away from the nest. Until they are big enough to scatter and be on their own, the parents watch over and care for them much as a hen looks after a flock of chickens. A bullhead family out for a swim is something to see. Come out next spring and I'll prove it to you."

10

The Little Bee Box

"Do you know what a beeline is?" asked Tommy.

"Of course I do. Everybody knows that. It's a straight line between two points," replied Sammy. He sounded a bit annoyed. He thought it was a foolish question.

"And it is the shortest distance between two points," added Sue.

"Did you ever see one?" asked Tommy.

"See what?" growled Sammy.

"A beeline — a real one," replied Tommy.

Sue looked at her cousin sharply. "Stop kidding us," said she. "Of course we've seen straight lines, lots of them. Everybody has. Don't be silly!"

Tommy looked as if he felt a wee bit foolish. "I'm not silly, but I guess I was perhaps a bit stupid," said he. "What I should have asked is, have you ever seen a line of bees? When they are loaded with pollen and nectar and ready to start for home they don't waste any time. They know exactly where home is and they fly there in a straight line, a bee-line. When a lot of them have found a place where there are plenty of sweets they go back and forth as fast as they can fly. It makes a line of bees. That reminds me that I ought to go bee hunting instead of berrying today."

"Why ought you to go bee hunting? And just what do you mean by that? I never heard of hunting bees," said Sammy.

"I ought to go hunting those bees because I don't want to lose them," replied Tommy.

Sue wrinkled her nose at him. "Stop talking in riddles, Tommy," said she. "How can bees get lost? If they can and do, why ought you to try to find them? What will you do with them if you do find them?"

Tommy chuckled. It was a good-natured chuckle. "Sue, I forgot you don't know about bees," said he. "One day when there was no one around to see them, the bees in one of our hives over there on the edge of the Old Orchard left the hive with their queen. That is called swarming. We haven't the least idea where the swarm went. If I can find them, and they are where we can get them, we'll just bring them home and put them in another hive."

"You may, but not me!" declared Sammy with a decided shake of his head. "What made those bees leave the hive anyway?"

"The hive was getting crowded. When that happens the queen and most of the workers leave the hive and go off to look for a new home. When they do this there is always a new queen, a young one, left behind with a few workers to rebuild the colony. The old queen and her workers usually find a hollow tree somewhere and start a new home in it. It's fun to hunt bees. What do you say if we try it instead of going berrying today?" said Tommy.

That suited the twins. Tommy told them to wait for him while he went back and got his bee box. He soon returned, and in his hand was a little box about three inches square and about the same in height. Over a hole in the cover was fitted a piece of glass. This made it possible to look into the box to see what was there. About halfway down on one side was cut a slit in which was fitted a glass slide dividing the box in two parts. In the lower part was a bit of honeycomb with a little honey in it. The twins eyed the box with lively curiosity.

"Now we're all set!" cried Tommy. "Let's get busy and look for bees."

The three separated. Sue found the first bee and called to Tommy. With the cover of the box he deftly brushed the bee into the upper compartment and put the cover on. Through the glass they watched the bee buzz about angrily for a minute or two. Then she quieted down and Tommy deftly pulled out the glass slide. At once the bee discovered the honey in the lower compartment. Here was treasure trove indeed! Tommy placed the box on a fencepost and removed the cover. "Now," said he, "watch and mark the direction that bee flies when she leaves."

When the bee had loaded up with all the honey she could carry, she took to her wings. She didn't circle very high, for there were no trees near. It was easy to watch her. "She flew that way!" cried Sue pointing toward the Old Orchard.

Tommy nodded. "She is from one of our hives over there," said he. "She isn't of any help to us. We want a bee that flies in another direction."

So they separated to hunt for another bee. This time Sammy found one. It was soon in the little box on the fencepost. When it left, this bee headed in the same direction as the other. Several times the same thing happened, but Tommy was not at all discouraged. "You see," said he to his impatient cousins, "there are so many hives over there that most of the bees around here are bound to be from there."

At last a bee flew off in another direction. Both Sammy and Sue agreed on this. Tommy's attention had been drawn to something else at just that instant and he hadn't seen the bee leave. "You're sure about that?" he asked.

"Sure!" replied the two in chorus. "It must be from that lost swarm," said Sammy. "Don't you think so, Tommy?"

"I'm afraid not," said he. "Uncle Ben lives over in this direction and he also keeps bees. We'll just leave the box right here and see how long it takes that bee to return."

"Are you telling us you expect that bee to come back to this very box?" asked Sammy incredulously.

"I know she will," replied Tommy. "Probably she'll bring another with her."

Sammy looked skeptical, but after a short wait two bees were in the box. "Just as I thought," declared Tommy. "Those bees are from Uncle Ben's hives. It would take a bee just about this length of time to fly there and return. It's of no use to waste time on these."

Gently he brushed the two bees from the box and started off to look for another bee. He soon had one, and this time he placed the box on another post. As the bee left the box Tommy was jubilant. She had headed straight for the woods. "That's the girl we were looking for!" he cried.

"How do you know it's a girl?" demanded Sue.

"All working bees are girls," replied Tommy. "Did you see which way that one went?"

"Sure," replied Sammy. "She headed straight for the woods. What of it?"

"I know!" cried Sue. "There are no hives over in the woods, so that bee must be from the swarm we are looking for."

"Right you are, Sue. Those bees must have found a hollow in a tree or a log over there. Now we know where to look for them," said Tommy.

"Yeah, now we know where to look!" snorted Sammy scornfully. "I suppose we just go over there in the woods and look for a bee. I've heard of looking for a needle in a haystack, but that has nothing on looking for a particular bee in a forest."

Tommy laughed. "Be patient, Sammy. Now we know in which direction to look, but just to be sure we'll wait until the bees start a line," said he.

Tommy kept a watchful eye on the little box on

the fencepost while he explained some of the things he had learned about bees. He broke off abruptly to exclaim, "There she is! And she has brought another with her. We'll soon have a line straight from this post to the place where those bees are living, a beeline."

And so it was. From experience Tommy knew how long it takes a bee to carry a load a certain distance, leave it and return. Thus he could figure very closely the distance to the home in the woods of these particular bees. "It's a quarter of a mile from here to the edge of the woods, and I judge the tree must be a little short of that distance in," said he.

While two bees were in the box, Tommy slipped on the cover. Sighting a tree on the edge of the woods in direct line with the post on which the bee box was, he picked up the box and started straight for the tree. "Come along, the hunt is on!" he cried.

Excited and mystified, Sue and Sammy followed.

11

Sammy Loses the Line

Tommy stopped at the edge of the woods. He placed the little bee box on a post and removed the cover. The two bees crawled out, circled high, and flew straight into the woods. They flew high enough to clear the tops of the trees.

"What's the big idea?" demanded Sammy.

"We're a quarter of a mile nearer the bee tree than we were back there where we started," replied Tommy.

"Sure thing," Sammy admitted. "But we could see this tree from back there, so what's the use of stopping here now? What have we gained by leaving there when we had that line of bees working so nicely?"

Tommy laughed. "They'll all be coming here just as soon as those two who left us can pass the word along," said he.

So it proved to be. Soon a double line of bees was at work between the bee box and their home. Again Tommy trapped two bees in the box. Taking it with him, he walked a short distance at a right angle to the line of flight of the bees. He placed the box on another post and removed the cover. Away flew the two bees. Tommy watched closely their line of flight, then rejoined his cousins at the other post. On this post he had left a little honey and the line of bees was still working.

"What's the idea of taking that box way offside?" demanded Sammy.

"To fix a base line to complete the triangle," explained Tommy. He chuckled at the twins' puzzled looks.

"What triangle?" Sue asked.

"The triangle that will show us where the bee tree is," replied Tommy. "We'll call this bee tree triangulation, if you like," he added. "This is one end of the base line. That post where the bee box is now is the other end of this line. The line of flight of the bees from this post makes one side of the triangle. When the bees have a line working from the box over there we will have the other side of the triangle. Where the two lines meet the bee tree is bound to be. You see, all these bees belong to the same colony. Sammy, you get the line from here fixed in your mind and follow it as closely as possible. I'll do the same thing from the post over there. Somewhere in the woods we'll come together and right there we'll find the bee tree. But for goodness' sakes, don't get off the line! Now I'll go over there to the bee box and give the signal to start."

Presently Sammy got the signal and started slowly along the line. Sue had joined Tommy. As they entered the woods Sammy lost sight of them. For a short distance he kept to his line. Then he caught sight of Jumper the Hare. It was the first time he had ever seen a wild hare. He forgot the bees. He forgot what he was doing. He turned aside for a better look at the big rabbit. The latter hopped from cover to cover. Sammy followed. Suddenly he remembered what he was supposed to be doing. Alas, he hadn't the slightest idea which way to go. After a while he heard Tommy calling. There was nothing to do but go over and join Tommy and tell him they would have to start all over again. Tommy took it all good-naturedly.

Fortunately Sue was carrying the bee box with two prisoners in it. Going to the nearest open place where the bees could be watched, they were given their liberty and soon a new line was established.

This time Sammy kept to the line and Tommy kept to his. Finally the two came together.

"Now what do we do?" Sammy wanted to know.

"We find the tree," mumbled Tommy, with his head tipped back as he studied the treetops.

The twins did the same thing, but they didn't really know what they were looking for. Tommy knew. He had hunted bees before and knew all the tricks. "I've got it!" he cried presently. "It's that old hemlock. It's partly dead and there must be a big hollow in it. Look about two thirds of the way up that tree. If you look closely you'll see a knot-hole and some bees around it."

"I see them!" cried Sue, clapping her hands. "Aren't they the smart things! Whoever would think of looking way up there in that tree for honey."

Tommy chuckled. "Buster Bear would if he should come this way," said he.

Somewhat furtively Sammy looked around. "You don't suppose he will, do you?" he asked.

"Will what?" Tommy wanted to know. He had been studying the bee tree and not paying full attention to what Sammy was saying.

"You don't suppose a bear will happen along," replied Sammy.

Tommy smiled. "Not while we're around. Buster Bear is too bashful for that. So don't worry, Sammy," said he.

"What would he do if he should happen along here when no one was about?" Sue wanted to know.

"What would you do if you should find a box of candy and no one else was around?" asked Tommy.

Sue made a face at him. "How would he know there was honey in this particular tree?" she persisted.

"His nose would tell him that, I guess," replied Tommy. He went over to the foot of the tree and started to climb.

"What are you going to do?" cried Sue.

"Climb up and look things over to try to get an idea how big that hollow is," replied Tommy.

"You'll get stung!" warned Sammy.

"Not me," replied Tommy, and grinned down at his cousins. "I know bees and I guess they know me. You know I take care of all the hives at home. They really are my bees."

"I should think you'd be afraid of them," said Sue.

"If I were they'd know it and I couldn't do a thing with them," said Tommy, starting to climb. Presently he reached the dead part of the tree. "It's a deep hollow and they have some honey stored already," he called down.

"How do you know that?" asked Sue.

"There's a long crack where the sun shines a good part of the day. I guess this must have softened the wax. Anyway, a wee bit of honey has leaked out from that crack, and that means that they have filled quite a bit of space."

He climbed down from the tree and joined the others. "I want to see that crack," said Sammy and started to climb the tree.

"Be careful!" warned Tommy. "Don't do anything to disturb those bees. If you should do anything to make them mad it would be just too bad."

"Perhaps they'll think you are Buster Bear and try to sting you to death," cried Sue.

Sammy paid no attention. He kept on climbing while Tommy and Sue sat down on a log. Sue was full of questions about bees and Tommy did his best to answer them. They were so occupied that they didn't notice that Sammy was spending quite a long time up in that tree. A sudden yell brought them to their feet. They looked up just in time to see something dropping from limb to limb of the old hemlock. In a second Tommy realized that it was Sammy. He landed with a thump, scrambled to his feet and started to run, slapping himself as he ran.

"I hope you're satisfied," Sue called. Sammy was. A bee had stung him on the nose, and another had crawled inside his shirt before using her fiery little lance.

Tommy went to Sammy's relief. He found some wet mud with which he plastered the stung places. "What did you do up there?" he demanded.

"I didn't do anything for them to get mad about. Honest I didn't, Tommy. I only tried to cut out a splinter along that crack so as to get just a little of that honey," explained Sammy.

"And instead of honey you got stung. It serves you right, Mr. Smarty," declared Sue. "What do we do now that we've found those bees, Tommy?"

"We'll leave them alone for the present," replied Tommy. "I'll cut my initials on the tree. That will show anyone else who may happen to find the tree that the honey is already claimed. It isn't late enough in the season for the bees to have made enough honey to make opening that tree worthwhile."

Sue was still full of questions. "Is it true," she asked, "that each hive has just one queen and that she is bigger than any of the others?"

"Yes, that's true," replied Tommy. "She's more than just a queen — she lays all the eggs. She's the mother of the colony as well as the queen."

"She should be called the Queen Mother," declared Sue

"How does she get to be queen?" asked Sammy, still nursing his sore spots.

"Oh, she just eats her way to the throne," replied Tommy.

"Aw, go on!" growled Sammy.

"It is a fact," replied Tommy. "The egg the queen comes from is just like all the other eggs. It's the food she is fed while a baby, and plenty of room to grow in, that make her a royal princess. Then, when a new queen is needed, she is it. So you see it's the food that does the trick."

Sue looked at Tommy very hard as if to make sure he was telling the truth. "I never heard of such a thing," said she.

Tommy laughed. "You don't believe a word of that, do you, Sue?" said he. "Nevertheless, it's true. When a hive begins to get crowded the workers know it's about time to start a new colony. Those who leave the hive must take the queen with them because, as I have told you, she is the one who lays all the eggs. Those left behind must also have a queen, so they proceed to make one. They tear out the partitions between three adjoining cells, build a big cell where the three were, and leave in it one of the three eggs that were in the first three cells. The other two eggs they destroy. When that egg hatches the baby is fed a special food called royal jelly. On this she develops into a princess who will become queen when the time comes. All this is done before the old queen and her workers leave. Ordinary babies are fed honey and bee bread made from the pollen of flowers. So you see it is true that food can make a queen."

"I wonder what royal jelly is like," said Sue dreamily.

12

Jimmy Understands

Flip the Terrier was making his usual inspection of the dooryard to see if there had been any visitors in the night. So far he had found nothing to get excited about. At one corner of the house a large tile drainpipe had been set in the ground to carry off rainwater from the eaves. Wholly from habit, for never had he found anything of interest in it, he trotted over to it and looked in. Then he jumped back as if he had stepped on something hot. Hurriedly he backed a little farther. Then he began barking, and how! It brought Sue and Sammy to see what the fuss was about.

At sight of them the little dog barked harder than ever. He was beside himself with excitement. He made short rushes toward the corner of the house, then backed as hastily. He danced from side to side. Sue and Sammy looked all about but could see no cause for his excitement.

"What are you barking at, you silly dog?" cried Sue. Flip was doing his best to tell her, but she didn't understand dog language.

"Perhaps there's a hole under the house and he saw something go in there," suggested Sammy. He began to look for an opening in the underpinning. The nearer he got to the drainpipe at the corner, the more excited Flip became. Sue laughed. "You must be getting warm, Sammy," she said.

Sammy moved ahead toward the corner of the house. Flip became more excited than ever. Sammy noticed for the first time the drainpipe set in the ground. He moved forward quickly to look into it. "There's a cat in there!" he exclaimed. "It's a strange one, a black and white one. I'll take it out."

"Better not try it unless you know just how," said Tommy. Unnoticed, he had come up behind them. He was smiling broadly.

"Why not?" demanded Sammy. "I'm not afraid of a cat."

"You might get scratched," put in Sue.

"He might get something worse than a few scratches," said Tommy.

Suspicious, Sammy backed off a little. "Just what do you mean?" he demanded.

"That is a woods pussy, but not a cat," replied his cousin.

Sue and Sammy jumped back. "You mean — " Sue began and paused.

"I mean that is Jimmy Skunk," said Tommy, and laughed at the look of consternation on Sammy's face as he realized how very near he had been to disaster. "Evidently Jimmy fell in there and couldn't get out," continued Tommy. He approached the drain so he could look into it.

"I'm going to toss a stone in there and see what he'll do," said Sammy.

"You'll do nothing of the kind," retorted Tommy. "What he would do would be to make it very unpleasant around here for all of us for some time to come. We've got to get him out of there without frightening him. Flip must be shut up. He's likely to lose his head from excitement and we don't want anything like that to happen."

"How are you going to get him out of there?" demanded Sammy.

"I'm going to lift him out of there," said Tommy.

"What with?" asked Sue.

"With my hands. What do you think?" retorted her cousin.

"You don't dare!" declared Sammy.

"That's true if you mean the way I would pick up a cat," replied Tommy. "That skunk wouldn't understand what I was doing and might resent it. I'm going to pick him up by his tail. I have read that this can be done without unpleasant results if the animal is lifted quickly and held so that it's free of everything. I've picked up little skunks that way, but never a big one like this. However, I've always found Jimmy a gentleman and I think he will be one now."

Tommy stooped over the drain. The other two backed off a little farther. The skunk's tail was where Tommy could get hold of it and he reached for it. "You better not!" shrieked Sue, dancing up and down with excitement.

Tommy grinned and continued to reach for the tail. He did it slowly. However, when he had firm hold of the tail he did move quickly. He lifted the skunk smoothly and easily, but so quickly that before the skunk knew what was happening he was held out helpless in midair.

Jimmy didn't struggle. He seemed to understand fully that he was being helped. Tommy took him out of the yard and across the road. All the time he talked to him soothingly. In the field beyond was

a deserted woodchuck hole. In front of this Jimmy was gently put down, and his rescuer backed away hastily. The big skunk merely looked back over his shoulder and with dignity entered the hole and disappeared.

"Didn't I tell you that Jimmy is a gentleman?" asked Tommy.

"Why didn't he use that scent gun of his?" demanded Sammy.

"I don't know for sure, but I suspect that held in that way with his feet off the ground and not touching anything he couldn't shoot," replied Tommy.

"He didn't want to," asserted Sue. "He knew you were helping him out of trouble."

Tommy nodded in agreement. "That's what I think myself," said he. "Animals and birds know much more than most folks think they do. If they are in trouble they know when we are trying to help them. I'm pretty sure that the skunk couldn't use his scent when I was holding him that way by the tail, but he could have used it when I put him back on the ground. He could have and didn't. I helped him and he knew I was his friend."

"What good is a skunk, anyway?" Sammy wanted to know.

The question went unanswered just then, for Tommy heard his father calling him. Then the matter was forgotten. Later that day the three went berrying. Suddenly from almost under Sue's feet a big rabbit scampered out, his white tail bobbing up and down as he ran farther and farther into the blackberry patch.

"Oh, it's Peter Rabbit!" cried Sue.

"Where did he go?" demanded Sammy.

"Over in there," replied Sue, pointing to the middle of the berry patch. "What are you going to do, Sammy?"

"Go in there and drive him out. I want to see him," replied Sammy.

"You'll get all scratched up. Besides, I don't want Peter scared. I don't see how he gets around through those briars as fast as he does. They don't seem to bother him a bit," said Sue.

"Of course they don't," replied Sammy with an air of superior knowledge. "Don't you see those little paths all clear of briars and just big enough for a rabbit? He made them himself."

"How do you know so much, Mr. Smarty?" demanded Sue.

"I read about it," replied Sammy.

Slowly he made his way toward the rabbit's retreat. With every step the briars clutched Sammy. They scratched his face. They scratched his hands. But Sammy was persevering and at last was almost in the middle of the patch. Then things happened suddenly. He caught a glimpse of the rabbit. At the same time he felt a sharp pain in one leg that brought a yelp from him. It was as if a red-hot needle had been thrust into his leg. A second later he was stabbed in the back of the neck and on one ear. The air seemed filled with angry insects. He

had disturbed a yellow jackets' nest. Sammy was on a hot spot. He dropped his pail right there and got out of the berry patch in a hurry. The yellow jackets followed him, and one of them stung Sue as she ran. She had dropped her pail too.

When Tommy saw his cousins he didn't need to ask what had happened. He was sympathetic and promptly plastered the stings with wet mud.

"I guess I didn't use my eyes as I should have," confessed Sammy. "I was looking for that rabbit and didn't see the hornets' nest. I must have bumped right into it."

Tommy shook his head. "You wouldn't have seen it if you had been looking for it," said he. "It's probably in the ground and you stepped close to the entrance. You were just out of luck. I'll get your pails tomorrow."

"I'll say I was out of luck," growled Sammy.

On the morrow Sammy felt so much better that he decided to go along to point out just where the wasps' nest was. Sue joined him. She hoped to see Peter Rabbit again. At the edge of the berry patch they stopped.

"It was right over there in the very middle," said Sammy. "You'll find my pail right there. But if you take my advice, you'll leave it right there."

"I guess I can get the pail without disturbing the wasps," said Tommy. Slowly and carefully he made his way in. He found the pail and picked it up. Then he began to look around. "Come on in here, Sammy. There's something I want to show you," he called.

Sammy shook his head vigorously. "Not me! I was in there yesterday and that was enough for me," said he.

"There's nothing to be afraid of. All you have to

look out for is briars. There isn't a wasp here," called Tommy, and began to stamp about.

At last Sammy ventured in. "Where are they?" he demanded suspiciously.

"Ask Jimmy Skunk. He knows," chuckled Tommy.

"Meaning what?" Sammy growled.

"Simply that Jimmy was here last night and found the nest. He dug it open and ate all the wasps and their young. The nest was partly in the ground and partly under this stump. Jimmy made a good job of it. All the wasps were in there for the night. It was cool and that made them dopey. So Jimmy ate them and probably didn't get stung once. Where Jimmy Skunk is you don't find many yellow jackets around. Now you know in part what good a skunk is," Tommy explained.

"And I didn't suppose he was good for a thing except his fur," confessed Sammy.

"He is one of the most useful animals on a farm because he destroys mice and injurious insects," said Tommy.

13

Sue Keeps a Secret

Tommy had just returned from driving the cows to pasture. "Peter Rabbit is a papa now, but I doubt if he knows it," he announced.

"Why do you doubt he knows it? Why shouldn't he know it?" asked Sammy.

"Probably Mrs. Peter thinks the babies safer if their pa doesn't know where they are. Not knowing there are any, he won't go looking for them," said Tommy.

"I don't see what harm knowing where the babies are could do. Would he hurt them?" Sue asked.

"He might not hurt them himself, but he might give away the secret of where they are to someone who would hurt them. The only way to keep a secret is to keep it. Mrs. Peter keeps it," replied Tommy.

"Do you know where they are?" demanded Sammy.

Tommy's eyes twinkled. He nodded. "Yes," said he, "I found them by accident this morning."

"Oh Tommy, will you show them to us? I would love to see baby rabbits," cried Sue.

Tommy shook his head. "I can't, Sue," said he. "It's a secret, Mrs. Peter's secret. Besides, I wouldn't dare to," Tommy replied.

"You're a mean thing, Tommy Brown! We wouldn't hurt those babies and you know it," sputtered Sue.

"I know you wouldn't, Sue, and you wouldn't mean to give the secret away. Just the same, you probably would," replied Tommy.

"Why, Tommy Brown, you know I wouldn't! I can keep a secret as well as you can," retorted Sue.

Her cousin's good-natured face broke into a broad grin. "I know you wouldn't do it intentionally, Sue. But you might give the secret away without meaning to," said he.

"How?" spoke up Sammy.

"We couldn't visit those babies without leaving a trail. Later any one of several who would like nothing better than a dinner of baby rabbits might follow that trail right straight to them — a dog, a cat, a fox, a skunk. They all have the trick of following a man's trail to see what he is about, and tragedy often results. Many nests of birds are found by enemies in just this way. That's why when I find a bird's nest I rarely visit it again until the young have flown," explained Tommy.

"I guess if we hunt for it we can find the hole those baby rabbits are in," boasted Sammy.

"Did I say they are in a hole?" asked Tommy.

"Well, if they are not in a hole where are they? Rabbits live in holes in the ground," said Sammy.

"Do they?" countered his cousin most provokingly.

Just then there was an interruption, and it was several days later before Sammy brought up the subject again. He had just returned from the pasture. He was hot, uncomfortable, and feeling a bit out of sorts. "I don't believe there are any baby rabbits," he declared grumpily. "I bet there isn't a hole anywhere around I haven't looked in."

"I didn't say those babies are in a hole in the ground. They are in a nest," said Tommy.

"All right, Tommy, they're in a nest. But the nest must be in a hole," retorted Sammy.

"Supposing the nest is in a hole and you find the

right one. How will you know the nest is there? Those holes are deep, and Mrs. Rabbit certainly wouldn't make her nest up near the entrance," insisted Tommy.

Sammy looked a bit nonplussed but rose to the occasion. "I'd dig it out," said he.

"Have you dug open all those holes you found?" inquired Tommy.

"No," admitted Sammy. "I haven't dug open any of them."

"I'm glad of that," replied Tommy. "You would have ruined a lot of good homes and you would have done a lot of hard work for nothing. Mrs. Rabbit's nest is not *in* the ground but *on* it!"

"But rabbits do live in holes in the ground. I'm from the city but I know that much," protested Sammy.

"European rabbits do, but not American rabbits like our cottontails. They sometimes use holes, usually those dug by others, for shelter or to escape an enemy, but they don't live in them or use them for nurseries," declared Tommy.

Sue giggled. "So you've been wasting your time, Sammy," said she.

"No he hasn't," Tommy said quickly, noticing Sammy's look of chagrin. "He knows now where all those holes are. Later he will have a chance to get acquainted with some of the owners."

"I think it's mean of you not to at least tell us what sort of place Mrs. Rabbit uses for a nursery," protested Sue. "She must hide those babies somewhere."

"She does, right out in the open," replied Tommy, and that was all they could get from him.

Two days later Sue, crossing the meadow on her way to the pasture to look for some berries, happened to glance down just in time to avoid stepping on a small mat of dry grass. She wondered if there might be a mouse under it. With the stick she was carrying she lifted the edge of it, then squealed with delight. Stooping, she gently lifted a little blanket of grass and fur to count five wee rabbits

lying flat and still. How she longed to pick them up and cuddle them! Instead she carefully replaced the little blanket over them, looked hastily all about to see if she was observed, decided she wasn't, and went on her way. She had discovered Mrs. Rabbit's secret and she meant to keep it. Tommy was the only one she told. She knew that Sammy would want to go straight over there. He wouldn't hurt those babies. No indeed! But he wouldn't be Sammy if he didn't want to keep visiting that nest just to see how the bunnies were growing. That wouldn't do at all.

When she told Tommy he asked if she had seen Mrs. Rabbit. Sue shook her head. "I looked everywhere for her but I didn't see her," she confessed. "Do you suppose she was squatting in the grass somewhere near?"

"Not likely," said Tommy. "Probably she was watching you from the briar patch."

"She couldn't have been so far away as that," Sue protested. "The nest is way out on the meadow in deep grass, and not a tree or a bush near it."

Tommy laughed. "Wouldn't think of looking out there for a rabbit's nest, would you?" said he.

"I certainly wouldn't," agreed Sue.

"I guess that's the way Mrs. Rabbit figures it,"

said Tommy. "She may not be as smart in some ways as others, but when it comes to hiding her nest she is smart enough to fool most people most of the time. So she made her nest way out in the open meadow where no one would be likely to look for it."

"How can she go to it without being seen? From a distance I watched and watched, but never had a glimpse of her," said Sue.

"She visits her babies after dark. I have found her nest before and watched, but never have seen her visit the babies," replied Tommy.

It was a few days later that Tommy suggested they all visit the nest. "It's safe to do so now for the babies have left it," he explained.

"Have you been there again?" Sammy demanded.

"No," was the prompt reply. "I haven't been near it since I first found it."

Sammy looked at his cousin suspiciously. "Then how do you know they've left the nest?" he wanted to know.

"I saw two of them in the briar patch this morning. Now if you want to see that nest you couldn't find, I'll show it to you, or Sue will," said Tommy.

Sammy looked from Tommy to Sue and back.

"What does she know about it?" he demanded.

"She found it by accident and kept the secret," replied Tommy. "Come on now, and perhaps we'll see some of the babies. Anyway, we'll see a rabbit's nest."

At the nest the little blanket of grass and fur had been pushed to one side. The nest was empty. Sammy was peeved. "I wanted to see those little rabbits," he grumbled.

14

Sue Tries Detecting

"Look, Tommy! Someone or something has taken funny bites out of this roseleaf. They're almost perfectly round. Whoever did it must have a round mouth, I guess," exclaimed Sue.

"You'd be surprised," chortled Tommy. "If I should tell you, you wouldn't believe me."

"I would so," retorted Sue indignantly.

Tommy shook his head. "No, you wouldn't. Sammy wouldn't either. What's more, I wouldn't blame you. So I am not going to tell you, not now anyway. I'll make you a proposition. I'll give you two days to find out how the round holes at the edges of the roseleaves are made. Let's see how good you are as detectives. It will give you a chance to prove you have learned to use your eyes since you came here."

"I guess our eyes are as good as yours any day," growled Sammy.

"Then why do you and Sue want me to tell you who takes the round bites out of the roseleaves? Since we've stood here talking about it, I've seen two bites taken out of a leaf on that bush," replied Tommy. His eyes twinkled mischievously.

Sue and Sammy stared at the rosebush, then looked hard at Tommy. "It's true," said he.

"I don't believe it. I think you're spoofing us," declared Sammy flatly.

"I didn't think you would believe me, so you can't make me mad. I'll give you two days to find out who bites the roseleaves," replied Tommy. He walked away whistling.

"He thinks he's smart," snorted Sammy.

"I think so too," replied Sue rather surprisingly. "He saw something here that we didn't see, and we were right here with him all the time. Come on, Sammy, and show him we can find out things if we try. We'll just watch this bush until we find out who or what bites pieces out of the leaves."

Sammy shrugged. "Not me," said he. "You can watch that old bush if you want to, but I don't care who bites the leaves." Sammy started off on business of his own.

"Whoever did the biting may not come back again, or if they do, may come while I'm not here and I won't know," thought Sue. "I know what I'll do; I'll pick off all the leaves that have been bitten. Then I can tell if any have been bitten while I'm away."

Picking the leaves, she discovered that not all the pieces taken from them were round. In some cases long pieces had been taken out as if two bites had been taken so close together they overlapped. Bees were busy among the roses. A butterfly alighted close by, slowly opening and closing its wings. But nobody came to bite the leaves. Anyway, Sue didn't see anybody, and when at last she went into the house no leaf had been bitten. Sometime later she returned for a look at the leaves. From one, two long pieces had been taken, one on each side of the center rib so that the leaf was almost cut in two.

Bees were still visiting the roses. Sue saw one on a leaf, but gave it no thought. She didn't even notice that it was different from the honeybees. After this bee had flown away she happened to glance at the leaf. A round bite had been taken from it. Could it be? It couldn't be! Yet she was almost sure that when she first saw that bee on the leaf no bite had been taken from it. Sue suddenly became greatly interested in bees, but though she watched carefully for a long time she saw none on the rose-leaves, nor were any more bites, round or long, taken from them.

The next morning Sue was out bright and early to watch the rosebush. At last a bee alighted on a leaf. She watched it closely and for the first time

she really saw it. It wasn't like the honeybees and it wasn't like the bumblebees, the only bees with which she was familiar.

This bee was very busy, as bees usually are. At first Sue couldn't decide just what it was doing. Then she decided that it was eating the leaf. Was it possible that it would or could at one time eat enough to make one of those round holes?

"I thought bees lived on honey and pollen from

flowers," said Sue to Tommy, who happened along.

"So they do," replied Tommy.

"That one there is eating a leaf," said Sue. She pointed to the bee she was watching.

"Guess again," replied Tommy with a provoking grin, and went on his way.

Sue frowned. "Now what did he mean by that?" she muttered, and again turned her attention to the bee. A moment later she was racing after Tommy. She was quite out of breath when she caught up with him. "Bees do it!" she panted excitedly.

"Bees do what?" asked Tommy, pretending he didn't understand.

"Make those round holes in the leaves. I saw a bee make one of them. I thought it was eating the leaf but it wasn't; it was simply cutting it. It cut out a round piece and then flew away taking the piece with it." Sue's tongue flew so fast it almost tripped over itself.

"You don't say," teased Tommy.

Sue made a face at him. "Stop teasing and tell me why the bee carried off that piece of leaf," said she. "Has it been taken to the hive? Is it for food?"

"The answer to both questions is no," said Tommy. "To begin with, that bee you were watching wasn't a honeybee. Honeybees are social bees. They live together in a colony. That bee you saw was a solitary bee, living alone. She is called a leaf-cutter. I don't have to tell you why."

"No, you don't. But what was she going to do with that piece of leaf?" asked Sue.

"Let's see if we can find out," replied Tommy.

"I feel like a real detective," said Sue as the two of them prepared to watch the rosebush. "I found out for myself that it's a bee that cuts those leaves."

"But you didn't finish your job, so now we've got to do some more detecting," said her cousin.

"What do you mean by saying I haven't finished my job?" demanded Sue.

Tommy chuckled. "You watched the goods stolen and found who the thief is, but you didn't follow up to find what became of the stolen goods. I guess it isn't quite fair to call that leaf-cutter a thief. I guess she has a perfect right to those pieces of leaves."

"Will she eat that piece I saw her take?" Sue wanted to know.

"If I should tell you what she does with it there wouldn't be any fun in seeing for yourself. Here comes Sammy. Hi, Sammy! Stay with us awhile and learn to be a detective like Sue," called Tommy.

Sammy pretended he wasn't interested, but when the bee returned and began to cut a piece of another leaf, he watched as eagerly as did the others.

"Don't take your eyes off her," said Tommy. "When she gets that piece cut out she'll start for home and fly straight there. We'll get the line of flight before we lose sight of her."

"There she goes! Oh, there she goes!" cried Sue excitedly. She jumped to her feet to start after the bee. "Oh, she's gone!" she cried a second later. Sammy looked quite as chagrined as did she.

Tommy laughed. "Come on, we'll follow the trail," said he.

"How can we follow a trail when there isn't any?" demanded Sammy.

"We've got a clue, haven't we? All a good detective needs is a clue," replied Tommy.

"If you've got a clue you've got more than we have," grumbled Sammy.

"I know!" cried Sue. "We've got the direction."

"Right," replied Tommy. "As you know, when a bee starts for home it goes in a straight line. Come on!"

He led the way toward the woodshed, which was open on the side facing them. In the shed was a lot of wood neatly piled in stove lengths. "A straight line from where we last saw that bee would end somewhere in this pile of wood. We'll do our watching here instead of over by the rosebush," said Tommy. He began studying the ends of the sticks of wood so neatly piled there in the shed.

"I suppose you're looking for clues," said Sue.

"You guessed it," replied Tommy.

"What sort of clues?" Sammy asked.

"Holes," replied Tommy, "or at least one hole in the end of a stick of wood, a hole about the size Mrs. Leaf-cutter made in the leaves. If I'm not greatly mistaken there is one in the end of that stick up there." Tommy pointed to a stick near the top of the pile. As they looked, a bee came out of the hole and flew away.

Sammy was for climbing up and getting that stick right away, but Tommy suggested they wait for the bee to return. Presently she did return and alighted on the end of the stick. They could see that she was carrying a bit of green leaf. She entered the hole and pulled in the bit of leaf after her. As soon as she left for another cutting of leaf Tommy climbed up and carefully withdrew the stick from the pile.

"What made that hole?" asked Sammy as he examined it. It was about the size of, or perhaps a little larger than, the circumference of an ordinary lead pencil.

"Mrs. Leaf-cutter!" replied Tommy. "You see she's a carpenter as well as a cutter of leaves. This wood is rather soft, a little decayed as you can see. We'll split the stick and see what's inside."

When the stick was split it revealed a tunnel several inches long. Nearly filling one half of the divided tunnel were what looked like green capsules. Carefully Tommy picked one out. As it lay in Sue's hand it looked more than ever like a capsule you would swallow for a dose of medicine. It was composed of pieces of leaf seemingly cemented together. The sides were the long pieces and the ends were closed with caps made of the circular pieces cut from the leaves.

"How could an insect do all that?" demanded Sammy.

"I don't know how she did it, but she did it," replied Tommy. "She cut this tunnel and she made all these little cells, a lot of work and a lot of skill, if you ask me. And that isn't all. Before she sealed them with those little green caps she partly filled those cells."

With the point of his knife Tommy carefully opened the cell in Sue's hand. It was partly filled with a sort of paste and on this was one tiny egg. "That stuff is pollen and nectar and it would have been food for the young bee that would have hatched from this egg if we had left it alone," Tommy explained.

Just then the bee returned with a bit of green leaf. She began flying uncertainly about the opening where the stick of wood had been pulled out.

"The poor thing! It's a shame to destroy her home after she worked so hard to make it and it's so wonderful. Can't you put it back somehow, Tommy?" cried Sue.

Tommy could and did. He tied together the two parts of the split stick and returned it to its place in the woodpile.

"And a little bee did all that!" said Sammy, as if he could still hardly believe what he had seen.

15

The Fairy Bottles

The three cousins were on the way to the old pasture for berries. Sue turned aside to peek into the briar patch hoping to get a glimpse of the baby rabbits living there. Her eyes were becoming sharper every day and there was little she missed. Now she discovered something that put all thought of baby rabbits out of her head.

"Tommy, the fairies have been here!" she cried.

"Huh!" sniffed Sammy. "Sue's always finding places where the fairies have been, but she never finds a fairy. I wonder what she has found now."

The two boys joined Sue. "Look!" she cried as they came up. "If a fairy didn't make these, tell me who did." She pointed to a bush at the edge of the briar patch, and without waiting for a reply continued: "Those are fairy water bottles. I know they are. They can't be anything else. No one but a fairy could have made them. Now, Tommy, don't you dare tell me there are no fairies!"

Tommy gave her an appreciative smile. "I guess you're right, Sue," said he. "If being small and having wings makes a fairy, a fairy it was that made these little bottles, or jugs, or whatever you please to call them." On a branch of the bush were several objects that did look very much like tiny bottles of brown earthenware. "But they're not water bottles. They probably are full of something, but it isn't water. I know that one at least is full, for it's sealed up," Tommy added.

"If it isn't full of water, what is it full of?" asked Sammy.

"Little caterpillars," replied Tommy. He smiled at the look on the faces of his cousins.

"Not really!" cried Sue.

"Yes, really," retorted Tommy, and added, "Here comes the fairy now, and she's bringing a small caterpillar."

"That?" exclaimed Sammy. "That's no fairy. It's a — " Sammy hesitated.

"Wasp," Tommy finished for him. "Just a wasp bringing home the bacon."

Right away Sammy wanted to know what was

meant by bringing home the bacon. It was evident
that he suspected a joke of some sort.

"Just that the wasp has brought home some meat
for one of her children and is about to put it in storage in one of those fairy bottles of Sue's," explained
Tommy. Sure enough, the wasp flew straight to
one of the bottles and dragged the caterpillar into it.

"What did he do that for?" asked Sammy.

"Not *he,* but *she,*" corrected Tommy. "Those
fairy bottles are nurseries for her children and she
made them herself. She is what is called a potter
wasp or jug-making wasp. Some folks call those
jugs instead of bottles."

"I like bottles best," Sue broke in. "They look
more like bottles than jugs."

"She makes them out of clay mud, fills them with

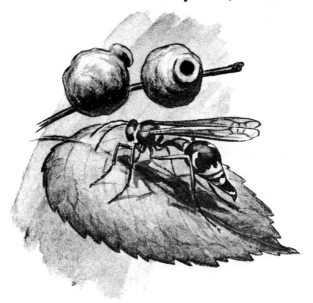

small caterpillars, and lays her eggs on the caterpillars," continued Tommy. "When the eggs hatch the young have ready right at hand a supply of fresh meat."

"Fresh meat," snorted Sammy. "Do you call bottled caterpillars fresh meat? How long do you expect those caterpillars to keep fresh in this warm weather?"

"Until they are needed," replied Tommy. "The caterpillar you saw her take in there just now isn't dead, merely paralyzed. That keeps it alive and fresh. Mrs. Potter is one of the mud wasps. Unlike the others she isn't satisfied with simple, plain, mud cells, so she makes these bottles."

"It truly is wonderful," said Sue softly. "It's just as wonderful as if she were a real fairy."

Later that morning on their way back from the pasture Sue insisted that they stop again at the briar patch. They found Mrs. Potter very busy at the entrance to one of the bottles. "She's closing it!" cried Sue.

"Sure," agreed Tommy. "She's sealing the entrance with mud. This means that she has left an egg in there with enough caterpillars to supply all the food the young wasp will need."

"I think she's wonderful, but she's sort of awful

too. Think of those poor caterpillars being kept alive to be eaten. I suppose that being paralyzed they don't know. I don't see why they can't have food that doesn't have to be killed," said Sue.

Tommy grinned. "I thought I saw you at dinner yesterday served twice with fried chicken," he teased.

"I didn't hear you say a word when we were watching Old Mr. Toad catching ants and swallowing them," added Sammy. He grinned at Sue too. "That was good ham we had for breakfast," he said.

Sue made a face at him and Tommy came to her relief. "I guess," said he, "that it's a basic law that life depends on living things. When you think of it, plants that we eat are living things. When she hunts caterpillars, the wasp is doing us a good turn and you shouldn't feel sorry for the caterpillars. If nothing stopped them they would wipe out all the crops we need for food. Those wasps do a lot of good. Funny, isn't it?"

"And I didn't suppose wasps were of any use to man. Makes life seem sort of complicated," said Sammy. "I don't see how the young wasp, sealed in that way, gets out."

"Cuts its way out with its jaws," replied Tommy.

"There may not be a really truly fairyland, but if there were I guess there wouldn't be anything more wonderful in it," declared Sue as the three made their way home. "Don't those wasps eat anything but caterpillars, Tommy?"

"I've never seen Mrs. Potter bring home anything but caterpillars," said he. "But she has cousins that don't go in for caterpillar steak so far as I know. Anyway, I've never seen the cave-dwellers with caterpillars, and I've watched them often."

"Cave-dwellers! That's a new one. Who in the world are the cave-dwellers?" cried Sammy.

Tommy's freckled face broke into its ready grin. "That's what I call them. Most folks call them mud daubers, but I like my name for them better. They belong to the group of solitary wasps the same as Mrs. Potter."

"Meaning what?" Sammy wanted to know.

"That they live and work alone instead of in colonies or big family groups as those makers of the big paper nests do. When we get to the house I'll show you some of their caves," was Tommy's reply.

Back at the house he led the way around to one side. There he pointed to what seemed to be a small mass of dried mud plastered on the brick foundation. "There are the caves, and there's the maker of them," said he as a slender-bodied black wasp alighted on the bricks and went to work, continually jerking her wings and turning about.

Examination showed that the somewhat shape-less mass of dry mud actually consisted of several adjoining tubes, rough on the outside, but, as could be seen in the one Mrs. Wasp was at work on, smooth on the inside. These tubes were made of mud worked into a sort of cement. Each little tube, or cave as Tommy called it, was about an inch deep. All but the one Mrs. Wasp was working on were sealed.

Tommy continued: "I suppose I shouldn't call Mrs. Wasp a cave-dweller because she really doesn't dwell in one. But her children do until they are grown, and she did too when she was young. Somehow whenever I see one of these mud homes I'm reminded of the cave-dwellers of old and the Pueblo Indians. Folks in some places in the world still live that way. That is why when I see one of these wasps I call her Mrs. Cave-dweller."

"I think it's a good name. It just fits," declared Sue. "Does she fill her caves with caterpillars? I suppose she does."

"That is for you to find out," retorted Tommy.

"I will," asserted Sue. "I can and I will!"

"Think you're smart," growled Sammy. "Playing detective again. I'll bet you don't find out."

"I bet she does," countered Tommy, and wished her luck.

The very next day Sue recognized Mrs. Cavedweller flying about in an open shed. She watched closely while Mrs. Cave-dweller visited every nook and corner and poked about under the eaves. Suddenly the wasp pounced, then flew away. She was carrying off a spider.

Sue ran around the house and was just in time to see Mrs. Wasp take the spider into an open cell. Sue squatted and watched patiently. She was well rewarded. Five times Mrs. Cave-dweller stowed away a small spider in the still open cell. She brought only spiders, not a single caterpillar. At last she brought mud instead of a spider. She was starting to seal the entrance. Sue knew then that an egg had been left inside. She watched until the job was finished. After a thorough inspection of the work Mrs. Wasp flew away. Sue waited awhile in vain for her return, then went to look for Tommy to tell him what she had found out.

"Some detective," muttered Sammy when he heard.

16

The Hole in the Dam

"I hope Paddy and Mrs. Paddy are at home," said Sue.

"They are. You needn't worry about that. But that doesn't mean that we'll see them. That depends on you," said Tommy as he held out a hand to help Sue across the brook.

"How does it depend on us?" As he spoke Sammy jumped the brook.

"If you tell them we're coming you won't see them," replied Tommy.

"Who's going to tell them?" demanded Sammy. He stepped on a dry stick and it broke with a loud snap.

"You are if you don't walk more carefully," retorted Tommy.

He was making good a promise he had made his cousins to show them Paddy the Beaver's pond deep in the woods. They were following the brook up toward the foot of the mountain. Sue sat down on a log to rest. "Wasn't there any pond at all up there before the beavers came?" she asked.

"No," said Tommy. "There was only the brook. The beavers turned it into a pond, and they did a good job. Come on, now." He started on. Presently he stopped for the others to catch up. They were a little out of breath and glad to rest. "In a few minutes we will be in sight of the dam," said Tommy. "From now on, no questions. No talking whatever. And watch your step. Keep right behind me and do as I do."

His cousins kept their tongues still and tried their best to walk as quietly as he did. When they came in sight of the pond he signaled them to wait while he crept on for a better view. Not a beaver was in sight. He beckoned the others to join him, then led them around below the dam. He had two reasons for doing this. By crawling they could get to the dam unseen from the water, and at the same time they would be downwind. The wind would be in their faces, carrying their scent away from the pond. On hands and knees they got to the dam. Very slowly Tommy began to lift his head to peep over. Then it happened. Sammy put a careless hand on a dead, dry twig and it snapped. Instantly from the other side of the dam and close to it, directly in front of them, came a report like a gun, and the sound of a heavy plunge. Water was thrown high in the air and some spattered over on them. It was all so unexpected and startling that both Sue and Sammy jumped, and before she thought Sue exclaimed aloud: "My goodness! What was that?"

"That was Paddy the Beaver saluting you and saying goodbye. He slapped the water with his tail as he dived," said Tommy as somewhat ruefully he got to his feet.

"But we didn't see him at all," wailed Sue. "Why did he slap the water with his tail? I almost jumped out of my skin. Why did he do it, Tommy?"

"He heard Sammy snap that twig and probably thought it was Buster Bear," declared Tommy. "He wasn't taking any chances himself, and he was warning others. He believes in passing along the word when he suspects possible danger."

"But we aren't enemies. We wouldn't hurt him," protested Sue.

"He doesn't know that. Anyway, he's a very bashful fellow. I doubt if he'll show himself again today, unless I can trick him into it," replied Tommy.

"How can you trick him?" asked Sammy. He was feeling very crestfallen.

While the others watched, Tommy carefully looked over the whole length of the dam. Near one end he stopped and seemed to be studying it at that spot. "I guess this is the best place," said he as he loosened the scout axe in his belt.

"Place for what?" asked Sue wonderingly.

"To chop a hole in the dam," Tommy explained.

"Do you mean you're going to chop a hole and let the water out of the pond?" demanded Sammy.

"That's the general idea," said Tommy.

"But what for?" cried Sue.

"So that you can see one or both of those beavers. Wasn't that the big idea in coming up here?" replied Tommy. His eyes twinkled.

His cousins were puzzled and looked it. "What has chopping a hole in the dam to do with that?" growled Sammy. He didn't like being teased.

"You'll see. But first we must make a good hide, or blind, where we can see but not be seen," said Tommy.

He proceeded to cut some hemlock branches, and with these made a blind from which they could watch the pond and dam without themselves being seen. Then he went to work on the dam. Sue's face wore a troubled look. "If you cut a hole won't that let all the water out of the pond?" she finally asked.

"It will if I make it big enough," replied Tommy, keeping his back toward Sue.

"I think it's a mean trick! I do so!" declared Sue indignantly. "If you're doing such a mean thing as that just so I can see a beaver, you may stop right now, Tommy Brown!"

Tommy's face had a suppressed smile as he turned to look at her. "It isn't as mean a trick as it seems, Sue," said he. "I'll cut only a small hole, one just big enough to let only a little water run out, just enough so that those beavers will know there's a leak in the dam. They'll want to fix it. They don't believe in putting things off. This time of year they haven't much to do. A little work will do them good."

"Just the same, I think it's a mean trick!" retorted Sue.

It was quite a job to cut even a small hole, for the dam was well built. Sammy helped, pulling out sticks as Tommy cut and loosened them, and digging out leaves and earth packed in between. Both boys were more or less out of breath and were drenched with perspiration by the time the water began to trickle through. As soon as a fairly good stream was running they joined Sue in the blind. They were glad to rest and have a chance to cool off.

Tommy had warned the others that they must keep as still as possible. They did for what seemed to them a very long time. It was very still there in the deep woods. Once the silence was broken by the harsh voice of Croaker the Raven as he flew over the pond toward his home on a distant cliff. Sammy's patience was first to give out. He became restless. He fidgeted. Tommy put out a warning hand. A brown head had suddenly appeared in the water close to the hole in the dam. It was Paddy the Beaver. For a moment or two he floated there with only his head above water. He seemed to be studying the hole. Then he swam in and climbed out on the dam beside the hole. Sue barely smothered a gasp as he dragged his big, broad, flat tail out of the water. It glistened in the sun like black rubber.

The beaver lifted his head and tested the air. Then he scrambled across the dam and down the other side only to scramble back a moment later and then slide into the water. He dived and was gone.

"Oh! Oh! Oh!" exclaimed Sue, but under her breath. Tommy said afterward that her eyes looked as if they were about to pop out of her head. Sammy looked no less amazed and excited.

Tommy chuckled. It was a soundless chuckle. "I told you I'd show you a beaver," he whispered. "Now if you can keep still a while longer you may have a chance to see beavers at work." He put a finger on his lips and nodded toward the water.

Swimming toward the dam, and towing a stick from which the bark had been peeled, was a beaver. Following was a second beaver, also towing a stick. The first one climbed out at the break in the dam, dragged the stick into the break and became very busy putting it in place. The other dived, and from the turmoil in the water below the hole it was evident that repairs below the surface were being made.

The two beavers left together, swimming on the surface for a little way, then disappearing under water. In a surprisingly short time they were back again, each with a stick. Paddy climbed out on the dam to work the sticks into place. Mrs. Paddy remained in the water, working part of the time under water. Just what she was doing couldn't be seen. She appeared to be bringing up from the bottom matted, waterlogged leaves and packing them between sticks in the break.

In a surprisingly short time the stream running through the hole began to grow smaller. Soon it was no more than a trickle. Not a minute had been wasted. The busy workers seemed to know exactly what to do and how to do it. It was a demonstration of perfect teamwork. To the three watchers it looked as if the sticks were pushed into the break in haphazard fashion, but the short time it took to reduce the flow of water was proof that those workers were too skilled for their work to be haphazard.

Sue was sitting in a cramped position. Trying to ease the strain, she leaned against one of the boughs of which the blind was made. It gave way. Instantly Paddy plunged into the pond. As he dived he hit the water a resounding blow with his big, rubbery, flat tail. It sent the water several feet in the air. Then two widening circles on the surface of the pond were the only indication of the swimmers.

Tommy got to his feet and stretched. "We won't see them again today," said he. "They have practically stopped the leak now, and after dark tonight they'll make sure of the job."

Sammy chuckled. "Now I know the meaning of that old saying 'to work like a beaver,' " said he.

"You saw some clever work, and you saw a bit of real courage. To come out on the dam and work in broad daylight knowing that something was wrong took a lot of courage," said Tommy.

17

The Chain of Life

"I still think it was a mean trick to cut that hole, Tommy. Just the same, I'm glad you did it. Oh! Oh!" Sue stood perfectly still looking across the pond to the shore beyond the big beaver house, which stood a little way out on the water. Her eyes were wide with delight and excitement. There at the edge of the water, her pretty head held high, ears spread wide, and her soft eyes staring straight across at the blind, was a deer, a big doe.

"Don't move," whispered Tommy.

For perhaps a full minute Mrs. Deer stood motionless. Then, her ears twitching, she lowered her head slightly and took a few dainty steps into the water. She put her slender nose down and began to drink. Sue almost squealed aloud as a pretty little spotted fawn came out from the brush and stopped at the water's edge beside its mother. Then a second fawn came out of the brush and joined the mother on the other side.

It was a beautiful sight, never to be forgotten. The sun was just right to cast their reflections in the smooth dark water as in a mirror. Behind them was the green backdrop of the forest trees. A little way out stood the high rounded roof of the beaver house, or lodge. In back of this and to the right, a long gray log lay partly in the water and partly on shore. Over all brooded the spirit of peace. Mother Deer went back in the brush and began to browse. The fawns gamboled along the shore. Finally they all disappeared.

"I used to look ahead to being old enough to go hunting and shoot a deer, but not any more," declared Sammy. "Not after that sight."

Tommy smiled. "We're two of a kind there, Sammy," said he.

They were just about to move out of the blind preparatory to starting for home when Tommy spotted a small brown head moving swiftly through the water over near the beaver lodge. "Billy Mink," he whispered.

The mink swam to the lodge and climbed out on the roof. They could see that he had a small fish. Just then a great blue heron appeared in what seemed heavy flight from the direction of the Big River. His head was drawn back between his shoulders so that he seemed to have no neck at all. His long legs were held straight out behind him like a thin featherless tail. At the other end of the pond, where the water was shallow, he alighted at the edge, raising his great wings high above his head before folding them. Then he stretched his long neck straight up and stood like a statue as he looked over the scene to make sure that all was well.

Once more the three watchers settled themselves comfortably. Smoothly the mink slipped into the water and disappeared. Over near the place where they had last seen Mrs. Deer not a breath of wind was stirring, but a bush had moved. There, it moved again! Three pairs of eyes focused on it. Presently a sharp face, seemingly hiding behind a black mask, appeared. Even at that distance could be seen the look of suspicious caution with which the pond and surroundings were studied. Satisfied that all was safe, the masked one came wholly into view. He was a big handsome fellow, wearing a brownish gray coat. He had a big bushy tail ringed with black bands. "Raccoon!" whispered Tommy. "He doesn't often come out in the daytime."

The big coon climbed up on the trunk of the fallen tree, walked along it to the end in the water, sat up very straight for a good look on all sides, then drank and daintily washed his long-toed front paws which looked so like small slim-fingered, human hands. He turned back and stepped down from the log, then started along the shore at the water's edge. With every step or two he stopped to study the shore immediately before him. Caution and alertness were in every motion.

"Looking for frogs," whispered Tommy. It was almost a soundless whisper.

A light splash to their right, and quite near, drew their attention. An old log, short but of good size, was half buried in the bank, half in the water, which was several inches deep at this point. A brown head popped out of the water at the end of the log. A moment later a chunky little fellow in a brown coat was out of the water sitting on the end of the log.

"A young beaver," whispered Sue delightedly.

Tommy shook his head. "Look at his tail," he whispered.

Sue and Sammy looked. The only thing about that tail that was like the tail of a beaver was its rubbery look. It was black, comparatively slender, narrow, pointed at the end, and flattened on the sides instead of top and bottom. "Muskrat," whispered Tommy.

The rat seemed to be very busy about something. "What's he doing?" asked Sue in an almost soundless whisper.

"Hunting for pearls," replied her cousin with mischief in his eyes. Sue made a face at him. Just then the muskrat dropped what he had been holding, dived and disappeared.

"Pearls!" snorted Sammy aloud.

Tommy smiled. "Well, he might have found one even if he wasn't hunting for it," said he. "He was opening a mussel, a sort of freshwater clam, a favorite food of his. Once in a while, say once in a blue moon, there's a pearl in one of those clams."

"Did you ever find one?" demanded Sammy.

"A teeny-weeny one, not big enough to count. But really good ones have been found," replied Tommy.

In the late afternoon light the little pond reflected in lovely detail the surrounding shore. Presently the smooth surface almost in front of them was broken by tiny rings that slowly widened, or slowly seemed to melt away. Now here, now there, they formed, spread and disappeared. Sue noticed them and wanted to know what made them.

"Watch that little fly over the water there just in front of us," said Tommy.

It was a tiny, gauzy-winged fly very near the surface of the water and flying somewhat erratically. It dipped, touched the smooth surface and disappeared. One of those tiny circles formed right there. They caught a glimpse of a small fish, probably a minnow, that had come up from below and taken the fly. A moment later a small trout made a little splash and a bigger ring as it jumped and caught a fly just above the water. They watched the trout swim in near the shore where the water was shallow. There was another splash and there was a big bullfrog with just the tail of that little trout protruding from his big mouth. He blinked, gulped and blinked again, but the tail wouldn't or couldn't go down.

"I call that a mouthful. Now where did that fellow come from all of a sudden?" cried Sammy.

Tommy laughed. "Probably he's been there a long time with just the top of his head and those big bulging eyes above water. He didn't move so we didn't see him. Grandfather Frog is a good waiter. I guess he believes in that old saying that all good things come to him who waits. He likes having his food come to him instead of going after it. That little fish caught and swallowed a fly, the frog caught and swallowed the fish and — look! There's Billy Mink running along the shore again and heading this way. Hold your breath and don't move!"

Sure enough, there was Billy Mink headed straight for the blind. Very slim and trim was Billy in his coat of rich dark brown. He looked just what he was, a member of the weasel family. Every movement was quick and graceful, almost too much so. His movements were almost snake-like as he made his way over and under and around logs and driftwood at the water's edge. Sometimes he darted back from the water a little way to investigate a bush or a little pile of brush. He was hunting, and there was little those beady eyes of his missed. In watching the mink the frog was forgotten.

Billy passed between the blind and the water. The three held their breath lest he suspect their presence and take alarm. Opposite the blind he stopped abruptly, one foot uplifted, and stared at the blind. Then he sat up very straight and they could see his white chin. He seemed to be trying to decide if that blind was worth investigating. Apparently he thought it was not, for he turned and with a quick bound continued on his way. He was running at the very edge of the water. Opposite where the big frog still sat with the top of his head above water the mink stopped. The frog started to bury himself in the soft mud at the bottom of the pond. He was just too late. With a bound the mink was in the water and had seized the frog. From the latter came a scream and then the mink was back on shore with his dinner, looking for a good place to eat it. Presently he vanished in that somewhat startling way which is one of a mink's characteristics.

"It is a regular chain of death — that fly caught by the little fish, the fish caught and swallowed by the frog, and the frog caught and eaten by that mink. Ugh! It's dreadful!" Sue screwed up her face and gave a little shudder.

"That depends," said Tommy.

"Depends on what?" demanded Sammy.

"On how you look at it," replied his cousin. "I call it the chain of life, and that is a much pleasanter thought. Each in turn gave up life that another might have food and live. I guess it's a sort of law of Nature."

Looking at it that way, Sue felt better and the matter was forgotten altogether in the excitement of seeing another deer come out to drink just as

they were making ready to start for home. It was a big buck, Lightfoot himself, Tommy said. He was very handsome, although his new antlers were only part grown and were in what is called the "velvet" stage. It was a perfect ending to a perfect day.

18

Where Was Mother Bear?

One of the strange facts of life is that what means much to one person may mean nothing at all to another. One sees black while another sees white. What a thing means depends on the one who sees it. The fly snapped up by a little fish, the fish swallowed by a frog and the frog becoming a dinner for a mink — to Sue this was a chain of death and so dreadful. To Tommy it was a chain of life, each in turn giving his own life that another might live.

"That chain isn't complete," Tommy explained. "Hooty the Great Horned Owl would love to dine on the mink, and the last link in the chain would be man. He would be the only one to kill without a real reason for killing, the desire to live. Come on now across the dam to find out if anyone whom we haven't seen has been around there lately."

Hardly had they stepped off the end of the dam

when Tommy pointed to a muddy place at the edge of the water, then hastily looked in all directions.

"What is it?" asked Sammy as he looked down where Tommy was pointing. Then his mouth fell open and his eyes seemed to be popping right out of his head. Sue's face wore the same expression. There in the mud was a huge footprint. It was something like the print a barefoot man with large, very wide feet and widely spreading toes might have made. But it was enough different for them to know that it was not the print of a human foot. There was a startled, questioning look on the two faces turned to Tommy.

"Bear!" said he with a rather feeble grin. "It's a print of a bear's right hind foot. Front feet make prints more nearly round. There is no mistaking the print of a bear's hind foot. No other footprint is so like that of man. Both man and bear are plantigrade."

"Meaning what?" mumbled Sammy.

"Meaning that in walking the whole foot is on the ground, leaving the print of heel as well as toes. Most animals walk only on their toes. Cats and dogs do this. Only a few put their heels down," Tommy explained.

"Know how I feel?" Sue broke in.

"How?" asked Tommy.

"Like Robinson Crusoe when he found the foot-print of Man Friday. Do you think that bear is anywhere around here now, Tommy?" As she spoke Sue looked anxiously all about.

"Not too near now, but she was right here when we started across the dam," replied Tommy.

"How do you know she was? And how do you know it's a she?" Sammy demanded.

"Because the mud in that print hasn't had time to dry at all, and because of the small print over by that fern. Mother Bear and her cubs were here only a few minutes ago," Tommy explained.

"Let's go home," said Sammy.

"Let's go right away!" cried Sue.

"There's no hurry," said Tommy. "Mrs. Bear is no more anxious to meet us than we are to meet her. This very minute she probably is hustling her cubs away from here as fast as she can."

"How do you know there's more than one cub?" asked Sue.

"I don't," was the prompt reply. "There may be three, or there may be only one. Usually there are twins."

"I would love to see them if their mother wasn't

around. How old do you suppose they are?" asked
Sue.

"They were born last winter, probably in late
January or early February," replied Tommy, quite
as if he knew all about it.

"Aw, go on!" exclaimed Sammy. "Their mother
was asleep then. Bears hibernate."

"Did I say they don't?" retorted Tommy. "Just
the same, those cubs were born when I said. They
probably weighed half a pound each and were about
the size of a rat. It was forty days before their eyes
opened, and they were more than three months old
when they came out of their den. Little bear cubs
are a lot of fun. I had one once. He got me in no end
of trouble, but he was funny."

"Don't you think we should be getting back
home?" Sue broke in nervously.

"A bear with cubs is mighty dangerous," spoke
up Sammy.

Tommy chuckled. "She would like to have you
think so," said he. "I met one once and she gave me
the scare of my life, but now I know it was largely
bluff."

"Are you trying to make us think a mother bear
with young isn't dangerous?" Sammy asked.

"No indeed!" replied Tommy soberly. "Nothing

at all like that. Certainly not! Any large animal cornered with young is dangerous. It's foolish ever to take a chance with them. A black bear can be, and sometimes is, a bad actor. For goodness' sake, look there!"

He pointed to an old log a short distance away. Above it poked a small head, and on the funny little face was a look of surprise and wonder. It was a cub. For a few seconds the cub stared round-eyed and fearful. Then it turned and scampered off whimpering with fright.

Sammy, all excitement, fears forgotten, sprang after it. "Let's catch him!" he cried.

The chase was short. Cubby went up a tree like a squirrel. He was a little fellow, but was as much at home in a tree as on the ground. As Sammy was about to climb the tree after him he was stopped by a shout from Tommy.

"Don't climb that tree! You've forgotten something!" shouted Tommy.

Sammy stopped and turned. "What have I forgotten?" he cried.

"That a baby bear probably has a mother somewhere around," replied Tommy. Meanwhile Cubby was doing his best to let Mother know he was in trouble.

"I — I — I — think we better get away from here," said Sue in a small voice that quavered.

At that moment there was a crash in the brush a little way off. With an ugly coughing snarl Mother Bear appeared. She stopped and stood up for an instant. My, my, how big she was! Her lips were drawn back, showing her big teeth. To the frightened eyes watching, they looked three times the size they really were. She looked up at the whimpering cub in the tree. He had begun to climb down. A warning growl stopped him. It stopped his whimpering too. He climbed back up a little way.

Mother took a step or two forward. She was still giving vent to that ugly-sounding coughing snarl. She looked as if she were about to charge. Even Tommy, who knew something about bears, was very uncertain of her intentions. Was this a bluff, or did she intend to attack? If she were bluffing, it was most realistic and convincing.

Just then there was a whimper from the brush back of her. It was from another cub. So there were two of them, as Tommy had suspected. For a minute or two that seemed an age, Mother Bear stood growling and snarling. Then she half turned to look back, but swung her head around again for another threatening growl. Thus, a few steps at a

time, stopping frequently to look back and snarl and growl a threat, Mother Bear retreated.

Just as slowly Tommy, Sue and Sammy backed away. The instant Mother Bear was lost to sight they turned and ran. How they ran!

"It was all a great big bluff," panted Tommy as they stopped to rest.

"Says you! But I notice you were as ready to run as we were," declared Sammy. He gave a hasty look behind.

"And how!" agreed Tommy honestly.

Sue giggled. "When we left home Sammy said we wouldn't find anything exciting out in the country," said she softly.

19

❧

Sue Has an Adventure

Sue liked to slip away by herself now and then, and go exploring. She had just gone a little way along an old road through the woods that adjoined the orchard when she saw running to meet her what at first she mistook for one of Tommy's pullets. "What are you doing way over here?" she exclaimed. Then she laughed as she saw her mistake and recognized Mrs. Grouse, miscalled partridge. They had met before, but that time Mrs. Grouse had promptly taken to her stout wings. Now Sue stood still. Mrs. Grouse came within a few feet, turned, ruffed up her feathers in a funny way, began to talk and started back along the old road.

"You lovely, funny thing!" exclaimed Sue. She began to follow slowly. Mrs. Grouse ran faster. She disappeared around a turn in the road. Sue stopped. It was very still in the woods. It was the first time she had been there alone. The strangeness of being alone in unfamiliar surroundings gave her a queer feeling. She decided to turn back.

Just then back around the turn in the road came Mrs. Grouse. She was running. Her feathers were now down smooth. In her eyes was an anxious look. She stopped almost at Sue's feet, turned, ruffed up her feathers, began talking in an excited, coaxing way, and started down the road again. Every few steps she looked back to see if Sue was following. She wasn't. She wanted to follow, but there was something so mysterious in the behavior of Mrs. Grouse that it increased Sue's uneasy feeling. Once more Mrs. Grouse disappeared around the turn.

"I'll go find Tommy and see if he knows what makes that funny bird act so," decided Sue. She turned back and began to hurry. She had gone only a little way when she heard a whir of stout wings and Mrs. Grouse alighted almost at Sue's heels. At once the same performance, the ruffed feathers, the anxious, coaxing cluck, the running a few steps and looking back, was repeated.

"She's trying to tell me something," thought Sue. Then in a flash she understood. "She wants me to help her. She wants me to follow her, and I don't quite dare to. If only I knew more about her and

her ways I might guess what the trouble is. Tommy
will know. He knows all about the things in the
woods."

She began to run. After her ran Mrs. Grouse.
Blacky the Crow, flying overhead, chuckled to see
Mrs. Grouse chasing a girl out of the woods. At the
edge of the woods Mrs. Grouse stopped, then turned
back.

Over in the barnyard Tommy and Sammy were
making a chicken coop. Tommy looked up to see
Sue running at top speed toward them. "What's the
matter, Sue? Is that bear after you?" he called.

Sue was out of breath when she joined the two
boys. "Tommy," she panted, "you remember that
big bird you called a part — part — part something
or other?"

"Partridge, Sue, only that isn't its real name. It
is grouse, ruffed grouse. What about it?" replied
Tommy.

"It chased me out of the woods just now,"
explained Sue. Then she told the boys just what
had happened. "Tommy, she wants help. I just
know it. And you've got to go help her," she finished.

"Why didn't you go help her yourself? I bet you
were afraid," said Sammy scornfully.

"I was, kind of," admitted Sue honestly. "I don't know the woods and I — well, I thought I'd better get you, Tommy. You'll know what to do."

The boys put aside their tools and followed Sue to the old road. Hardly had they entered it when they were met by Mrs. Grouse. She came within a few feet of them, turned, ruffed up her feathers, and began to move slowly down the road, all the time talking in grouse fashion.

"You were right, Sue. She's doing her best to get us to follow her," said Tommy as he took the lead. Mrs. Grouse began to run. After a bit Tommy halted. "Let's turn back now and see what she'll do," said he.

So they turned back. At once Mrs. Grouse came running after them. Her feathers were now smooth. When the party stopped Mrs. Grouse at once turned around and started back with her feathers once more ruffed up. "See that?" exclaimed Tommy. "There's something, or someone, ahead there she's afraid of, and that's why she ruffs up her feathers that way when she starts back. She knows we're her friends, so she keeps her feathers down when she comes after us."

They repeated the experiment with the same result. Then Sue protested. "It isn't right to tease her so. Let's find out what's wrong and help the poor thing if we can."

They moved on slowly, cautiously, silently, so as not to alarm anyone by their approach. Presently, ahead of them they saw a big branch of a tree overhanging the road. It was little more than arm's

reach above their heads. Mrs. Grouse flew up on this and remained there until Tommy was directly beneath her. By jumping he could have almost touched her toes. Her anxious clucking had given way to scolding.

Tommy looked carefully on all sides. A spot of red caught his keen eyes and he made out a fox nearly hidden under some big ferns off at one side. "So it's you, you old rascal, who's worrying Mrs. Grouse!" cried Tommy. He threw a stick in the direction of the fox. The latter got to his feet, grinned at Mrs. Grouse, and trotted out of sight. He was a good loser. The instant he was out of sight, Mrs. Grouse flew down and began to call softly. As if by magic eight young grouse appeared and ran to her.

"Oh!" cried Sue and Sammy together.

Mrs. Grouse fussed a little over her lively brood, then proudly led them away. She didn't hurry. She wasn't afraid. She wanted these new friends to see that fine family of hers.

"She's just like one of your hens with her chickens," declared Sue. "Do you suppose that fox was waiting all that time to catch one of them?"

"No doubt of that," replied Tommy. "The rascal knew they were hiding somewhere around here but didn't know just where. He was waiting for one to give himself away by moving."

Sue looked horrified. "Do you suppose the fox has caught any of that family of young grouse?" she asked.

"If he hasn't, someone else has," said Tommy. "I found the nest early this spring and there were twelve eggs. I know they all hatched. Now there are only eight young grouse. I have an idea that

Reddy or his mate could tell what became of the other four."

"I think he's dreadful," declared Sue.

"Don't forget that fried chicken and ham we talked about," said Tommy. "As a matter of fact it's probably just as well those young grouse were caught."

His cousins looked puzzled. "I don't get it," said Sammy.

"Probably they were the weaklings of the family," explained Tommy. "Of course I don't know that, but I do know that seldom are the smartest or the strongest of any family of feathered or furred folk caught by their enemies. It's the weaklings and the stupid who are caught first, and the race is better off without them. So by catching weaklings the fox and other furred and feathered hunters really are a benefit. Reddy does a lot of good by helping to keep the balance."

"What balance?" Sammy asked.

"The balance of life. Let Mother Nature alone and she keeps all kinds of life balanced. By that I mean she keeps the right number of each kind. Man is the boss upsetter of nature's balance. He kills too many of one kind, or he changes conditions so that another kind is favored more than others. When he clears land and plants it to grain and grass and other crops he makes a lot of easy food for rats and mice and other pests. As a result they multiply fast despite all man can do. Nature sends the fox, the hawk, the owl, and other predators to keep rats and mice in check. Man kills these checks because he doesn't take the trouble to find out the truth about them. So he upsets the balance. Reddy Fox is a smart scamp who is doing his part. Don't forget that!"

"You think a lot of that old fox, don't you," said Sammy.

"I do," replied Tommy.

20

A Mother's Love

Up ahead, in the bushes of the upper pasture, Flip the Terrier was trying to bark his head off. "He sounds excited. He must have found something," called Sue.

"He's always excited when he's allowed to come on a trip like this," replied Tommy, who was leading the way.

"Perhaps he's found a snake," ventured Sammy from the rear.

The three were after blueberries in the seldom visited upper pasture, now much grown with brush. As a special treat the small dog had been allowed to go with them, or, to be exact, go ahead of them. Presently Tommy came in sight of him. Flip certainly was excited. He danced from side to side. He made little forward rushes of a few steps, only to

stop and hastily back up. All the time he was barking.

"What are you so excited about this time?" called
his master.

Then he saw, a few feet from Flip, and facing
him, what he afterward described as a fighting fury
in a red coat. It was a fox, a vixen, as the female
fox is called. Her ears were laid back; her black lips
were drawn back so as to show her sharp teeth; the
hair of her coat was raised to make her look almost
twice the size she really was. Then Tommy saw a
half-grown young fox lying on the ground in back
of her and knew at once something was wrong with
it, which accounted for his mother's boldness in
holding her ground.

"What is it, Tommy?" called Sue as she and
Sammy hurried up. Then she saw Mrs. Fox. "Oh!"
she cried softly. "Oh, you lovely thing!"

With a sharp command Tommy silenced Flip,
then told Sammy to hold him. He pointed to the
young fox. "Something is the matter with that little
fellow. That's his mother with him. She wouldn't
have remained if he were all right. Both would
have been gone long before we came in sight. You
two stay where you are and I'll try to find out
what's wrong," explained Tommy.

Slowly he moved forward, all the time talking in low soothing tones to Mrs. Fox. Just as slowly she retreated. Her face no longer wore the ugly look with which she had faced the dog. Tommy was an old acquaintance, a friendly neighbor. She couldn't understand his words but she understood him. He was a friend. That was all that was necessary.

The trouble was soon evident. In jumping, probably trying to spring on a mouse or rabbit, the young fox had landed on a pair of parallel roots growing close together. One hind foot had landed between them, and the force of the jump had pushed them apart so that the leg slipped down between. The roots had snapped back like the jaws of a steel trap and the young fox was a hapless, helpless prisoner.

Tommy talked soothingly while he gently but deftly tried to work the leg free. Though he trembled, the young fox knew that a friend was trying to help him. Not once did he try to bite.

"What are you going to do with him?" asked Sue when the leg was free.

"Take him home and make sure that leg is right before I let him go free," replied Tommy.

"Give him to me for a pet," begged Sue.

Tommy shook his head. "Can't do it, Sue," said

he. "You may pet him all you want to, or all he will let you, while we keep him, but as soon as his leg is well enough we'll let him go. If he were a woolly little baby it would be a different matter. As it is he's too old to be robbed of his freedom. He never would be happy."

The young fox was carried back to the barnyard. After making sure that the bone was not broken, Tommy bathed the leg with liniment and bandaged it. A comfortable bed was made in a pen where Tommy had kept pets before. Food and water were placed where the young fox could easily get them. Then, at Tommy's insistence, the young fox was left undisturbed.

Before breakfast the next morning Sue was out to see the little patient. She ran back to the house with an odd expression on her face. "Tommy," she cried, "something queer has happened out there!"

"What do you mean?" demanded Tommy. "Is the fox dead?"

"No, but something else is. I think it's a young woodchuck. It's lying right on top of the pen. What do you suppose happened to it? How did it get there, Tommy?" replied Sue.

Tommy didn't answer but led the way out to the pen. Sure enough, on top of the pen was the body of a half-grown woodchuck. Tommy picked it up to examine it. It had been recently killed.

"Well, what about it? How did it get there?" demanded Sammy.

"Mother love put it there," replied Tommy teasingly.

"Stop talking in riddles," said Sammy. He looked a bit peeved.

Sue had caught the meaning. "Are you telling us that Mother Fox killed that chuck and put it up on the pen?" she asked eagerly.

Tommy looked at her approvingly. "Yes," he replied. "Either Father or Mother Fox killed that chuck early this morning, probably just after daylight, and brought it over here. Probably it was Mother. She was the one who was with the young fox when we found him, and she watched us take him away."

"But what did she bring the chuck here for?" Sammy was a bit dense.

"For the young fox of course. Don't be stupid," replied Sue, and Tommy laughed.

"But he couldn't get it up there. It seems to me that she was the stupid one," insisted Sammy.

"Of course he couldn't get it, but she didn't know that when she brought it," retorted Sue. "She left it anyway. Perhaps she thought we would give it to him."

"Which is just what we'll do," declared Tommy. Opening a little door in the pen, he tossed in the chuck. "Now we'll go to breakfast and leave the little fellow to eat his," he added.

The twins were full of questions. "Do you think she'll come again and bring him something more? If we keep watch do you think we can see her? Do you suppose the father fox will come too? Do you think she'll come during the day or only at night?"

"If she comes at all it will be after dark," Tommy assured them.

"It won't be dark tonight because of the moon," said Sammy.

"That won't stop her. With moonlight there will be plenty of shadows," answered Tommy.

Sue jumped up excitedly. "Tommy," she cried, "why can't we sit up tonight and watch for her?"

"That's an idea! Of course we can. Let's do it!" cried Sammy.

That afternoon Tommy prepared a hiding place in the barn. He bored three holes through which they could peep for a clear view of the pen. He arranged a plank on which they could sit comfortably. After supper, when the shadows had crept over the

barnyard, they took their places. It was very quiet
in the darkness of the big barn. The only sounds
were the occasional muffled stamp of a hoof, the
cows chewing their cuds, and now and then the
faint squeak of a rat. With nothing happening it
was hard to sit still, especially for Sammy. He stood
it for a couple of hours, then began to fidget. At
last he could stand it no more. "That old fox isn't
coming back tonight. I'm going to bed," said he.

Sue felt much as he did. In the dark Tommy
grinned as he led the way back to the house. Half
an hour later a shadowy form in the moonlight
leaped lightly up on the pen and lay there for some
time. When Mother Fox left, a young rabbit was
lying on top of the pen.

For several days the young fox was a prisoner,
but according to Tommy he wasn't in a prison but
a hospital. Sue always spoke of him as their patient.
At first the injured leg had been swollen, but now it
was back to normal. Mother Fox continued to leave
food at night. By day the young fox was petted and
made much of. Came a morning when Tommy announced they would set their prisoner free.

"Why?" chorused his cousins.

"Because I don't like being a jailer," said
Tommy. "As long as his leg was in a bad way that

fox was a patient in a hospital. Now that his leg is practically all right, keeping him confined longer would be making him a prisoner, and that's very different."

The young fox limped a little when he put weight on the injured leg. Much of the time he walked on three legs. However, Tommy was sure that he could use the injured leg if he really wanted to, and that once free he would want to. "We'll give him his freedom and his cure will be complete," said he.

"But supposing his leg isn't all right? On only three feet how is he going to catch enough to eat?" cried Sue of the tender heart.

"Don't worry, his mother will take care of that. That leg is all right. You'll see," retorted Tommy.

They headed for the upper pasture, where the young fox had been found. Near its edge Tommy gently put the young fox on the ground. For a second or two the little fellow stood still. Then, holding the injured leg off the ground, he took two or three steps. Suddenly he realized he was free. Down came that foot and away he raced for the shelter of the brush.

"I wish I could have had him for a pet," said Sue wistfully.

21

The Lion Hunt

"What's doing today?" asked Sammy at the breakfast table.

"How about a lion hunt?" replied Tommy. There was not so much as a trace of a smile on his freckled face.

Sammy looked at him suspiciously. "There are no lions in this country outside of a zoo, so what?" said he.

"How about the mountain lion?" asked Sue.

"I suppose you mean the big cat with several other names, puma, cougar, panther, catamount. That isn't a real lion. There's none of that kind around here now, although there used to be. But just the same, we have lions around. I saw signs this morning. How about seeing if we can find one?" replied Tommy.

Sammy's eyes snapped. "All right," said he,

"I'm game. Do I take my air rifle, bow and arrow, or just my slingshot?"

"Is it a game?" cried Sue. "I bet it is, and it sounds exciting. I'm for it. When do we start?"

After breakfast Tommy led the way toward the barn. Bowser the Hound and Flip the Terrier invited themselves to go along but were sent back.

"I should think they would be a help finding your old lions," said Sammy.

"No," said Tommy. "They wouldn't know one if they should see it. A funny thing about these lions is that they very often come close around houses, yet people living there never even know it. Sue was close to one the other day and didn't know it."

Sue gave him a sharp look. "I don't know what your lions are like but you can't scare me, Tommy," she declared.

"You're scared this very minute," teased her cousin.

"Girls always are scared of nothing," declared Sammy. "I bet your lions are only kittens, Tommy, or something like that."

"No, sir," retorted Tommy with a shake of his head. "First we'll look in back of the barn."

He peeped around a rear corner, then turned and beckoned the others to follow. A finger on his lips signified the need for silence. The others tiptoed after him. They were sure that this was a game, yet somehow they were excited.

Tommy stopped at a bare spot of fine sand close to the barn. He pointed to it. "They're here," he whispered.

In back of the sand was a dark opening under the barn. His cousins gave it a half fearful glance, as if they expected to see the head of a lion thrust out, or a pair of fierce eyes glowering at them from the darkness beyond. Then they looked down at the sand where Tommy was pointing. "There," said he, "and there, and there, and there!"

The two bent over to see better. They were looking for the footprints of some animal other than a lion, for they still thought Tommy was playing a game. The sand was fine and clean. In it were several small pits, varying from the size of a twenty-five-cent piece to that of a half dollar or a little larger. Each pit was perfectly round and slanted steeply to a point at the bottom, like a cone. No animal's footprint could make an impression like that.

"Those are not footprints," scoffed Sammy.

"Did I say they are?" demanded Tommy.

"You said the lions are here," Sammy accused him.

"They are," retorted Tommy.

"Where?" Sue demanded.

"There is one in each of those little pits," declared Tommy.

"Aw, talk sense!" said Sammy in a tone of disgust. "What's the joke anyway?"

Meanwhile Sue had been looking into one after another of the little pits. "There's nothing in them. All of them are empty," said she.

"Says you," retorted Tommy. "Watch that big ant running along there. Keep your eyes on it."

A large black ant was running between the pits this way and that, as ants have a way of doing when they are without a definite objective. It approached one of the little pits apparently unaware that it was there. A foot slipped over the edge, sending some tiny grains of sand rolling down to the bottom. Another foot slipped over, and more sand on the edge gave way. This time half the ant's body slid over the edge. The struggle to get back loosened more sand, and it and the ant slid to the bottom.

"Oh! Oh!" shrieked Sue. "There's something alive down there! There's something at the bottom that's trying to catch that poor ant!"

It was true. As the ant hit bottom the sand there

was vigorously stirred and something seemed to grab at the ant.

"I told you there was a lion down there. Watch now and you'll get a glimpse of it when it finally grabs the ant," replied Tommy.

The ant was frantically trying to climb the steeply sloping walls of the little pit. It would gain a little only to slip back. Then it appeared as if sand were being thrown up from the bottom. As the sand rolled back it brought more sand and the ant with it. The latter was seized and dragged down in the loose sand at the bottom.

"Didn't I tell you there are lions here?" cried Tommy triumphantly.

"Huh! They're nothing but insects," declared Sammy in a tone of disgust.

"But lions just the same — ant lions. That is what they're called. I didn't say what kind of lions we were going to look for, and I guess they look as bad to ants and to others that fall into their pits as real lions would look to us. Real lions stalk their prey, or lie in wait for it. Ant lions dig traps and then lie in wait. I think that's worse," said Tommy.

"The poor things," said Sue pityingly. She meant the ant, not the lion.

It did seem queer to call such little creatures

lions, but as Sue said, if one should grow as big as a real lion it would be worse to meet than any real lion ever was or ever could be. Tommy had scooped one out of its pit and they had a chance to see the big ugly jaws. He put the lion down where the surface

of the sand was smooth. Instantly it began digging in, moving backwards in a circle. It was starting a new pit. Fascinated, the three watched the curious worker enlarge and deepen the small pit.

"I wonder how those things ever learned that trick," remarked Sammy.

"What trick?" asked Sue.

"Trapping others. Those little pits really are traps. I don't know of any other creatures that set traps except man," replied Sammy.

"How about spiders?" asked Tommy.

Sammy grinned a bit ruefully. "That's so," he agreed. "A spider web is a sort of trap. I hadn't thought of that. What a lot of things we see and don't think about. Look over here in this pit. I can understand how anything crawling might tumble into one of these pits and be caught, but how one with wings can be so stupid as to be trapped is beyond me."

The others looked. Sure enough, there in that pit was a dainty little insect with a long slim body and four gauzy wings. As yet nothing had happened to it.

"I wonder if that lion in there is asleep, or afraid, or something?" said Sammy.

"Perhaps there isn't one in that pit," said Sue.

"Yes there is, but there won't be long," said Tommy.

Just then Gauzy Wings flew out of the pit and away. Sue gave a little sigh of thankfulness. "I'm glad," said she. "That little thing was too pretty to be caught by one of those awful lions. What did you mean, Tommy, by saying there wouldn't be one there long?"

Tommy chuckled. It was a provoking chuckle. "There isn't one there now," said he.

"How do you know? You haven't looked," said Sammy.

"I just watched it fly away," replied Tommy.

"What do you mean? Lions can't fly. They haven't any wings!" cried Sue.

"That one has, and all the rest of them will have," replied Tommy.

For a minute Sue stared at Tommy with her mouth open. "Tommy Brown, are you telling us that pretty thing we saw fly away is one of those horrid, ugly ant lions? I just don't believe it!" she snapped.

Tommy laughed. "I don't blame you one bit for doubting it, Sue," said he. "But it's true just the same. Is it any more wonderful than that a caterpillar changes into a butterfly or a moth?"

The hunt was over. Back at the house Sue suddenly squealed with excitement. "Look!" she cried. "Here are more of those pits right beside the doorstep!"

"Sure," said Tommy. "Some are there every year. I didn't show these to you because then we wouldn't have had any hunt. It wouldn't have been any fun."

"It's queer how you can look at things and not see them," remarked Sammy thoughtfully. "I noticed some of those pits the other day and thought they were made by water dripping from the roof. What has Sue found now?"

The Lion Hunt

"See!" cried Sue. "I guess one of your lions has learned to climb." She pointed to a leaf on the honeysuckle vine. Sure enough, on it was an insect that looked very much like an ant lion or enough so to at least be related.

Tommy shook his head. "It's a lion true enough, but not an ant lion. This one is a hunter, not a trapper. It is an aphid lion. It hunts aphids."

"What are aphids?" demanded Sammy.

"Lice, plant lice, among the worst pests we have," replied Tommy. "That lion is eating one now. I hope there are some more lions around, for they do a lot of good. What is it now, Sue?"

"It's the prettiest thing!" cried Sue. "It has pale green lacy wings and lovely golden eyes like Old Mr. Toad."

"Good enough! Now I *know* we will have some more aphid lions," exclaimed Tommy. "That is called a lace-winged fly, but it's really an aphid lion

grown up. That's Mrs. Lace Wing. I know it by those eggs on the leaf with her."

"Do you mean those funny little things that look as if they're growing on tiny stems out of the leaf?" asked Sue.

"Right," replied Tommy. "Those stems are of stiff silk. If those eggs were laid in a mass the first baby to hatch would try to gobble up all the rest. So mother separates them in this way. Sue, you sure are learning to see things."

22

Sue Finds a Nest

It was Sue who discovered Hummer the Hummingbird, he of the ruby throat, darting from flower to flower. Her cry of delight brought the two boys. They watched the tiny bird, whose wings moved so fast they were just a blur. His bright green coat and ruby throat flashing in the morning sun made him seem like a living jewel. In front of Sue, not three feet from her, he seemed for a moment to hold his place perfectly still save for the rapid vibration of his wings. Just in front of him was the crimson, tubular blossom of a trumpet vine. He moved forward two or three inches, thrust his long bill to the very heart of the flower, came straight back a few inches, then darted over to another blossom and repeated. Finally he flew to a maple tree in the dooryard.

"Why, that little bird actually backed away from

those flowers," gasped Sue, her eyes dancing with excitement. "Whoever heard of a bird flying backward!"

"Hummingbirds are the only ones I know of in these parts that can do it," said Tommy. "Hummer can stay still in the air, fly in reverse, or shoot away like a bullet. Some flyer, I'd say!"

"And he's such a tiny thing," cried Sue.

"I read somewhere that a hummingbird weighs little if any more than a new penny," spoke up Sammy.

"Yet it has all that any bird has in the way of bones and feathers, and may fly clear down to Yucatan to spend the winter. I wish I could find a hummingbird's nest. I've looked and looked but never found one," said Tommy. "I've seen one found by someone else."

"There he is on that dead twig up in the maple tree," cried Sue as they crossed the yard. "Oh my goodness, what's he doing that for?"

Hummer had left his perch and now, like a flashing jewel suspended by a long invisible thread, was flying in a great arc. Down almost to the ground, then up near the eaves of the house, down the other way and up, back and forth, back and forth he swung like a pendulum. "He's doing the giant swing!" cried Sammy. It was something like that and rather breathtaking to watch.

"He's showing off," declared Tommy. "You may be sure Mrs. Hummer is somewhere near, probably up in that tree, and he's doing his pendulum act for her benefit. Hello! There's another hummer!"

The exhibition ended abruptly and another started. This one was a fight. And what a fight it proved to be! With angry squeaks the two tiny fighters flew at each other, jabbing with their long needle-like bills, darting in and out, circling, dodging, moving so fast that it was impossible to tell one from the other.

"It's a fight to the finish and we have ringside seats!" shouted Sammy.

He was right. A moment or two later came the knockout, and one of the little battlers fell to the ground. He lay still while the victor darted back and forth above him, waiting for the count, as Sammy afterward described it.

"The poor little thing!" cried Sue. Impulsively she ran to pick up the little victim. As her fingers almost touched him he came to life and flew away.

"He's still groggy," declared Sammy, watching him out of sight. The victor had flown up to his former perch.

"Now I'm sure there's a nest or soon will be somewhere in the neighborhood," declared Tommy.

"What does a nest look like?" Sue inquired.

"Do you know what lichens are?" Tommy asked.

"Sure," said Sammy. "There are some over there." He pointed to a greenish-gray growth on top of an oak tree.

"Well, look for a lichen-covered knot or swelling about the size of a fifty-cent piece well out on a branch and maybe you'll have a hummingbird's nest," explained Tommy.

For the next few days much time was spent in looking for lichen-covered knots. All they found were just knots. Interest began to wane. Then, when she wasn't looking for it, or even thinking about it, Sue found the knot that wasn't a knot. She was lying in a hammock between two trees near the house. As she looked up without really looking, actually daydreaming, her idle glance rested for a moment on a little grayish bunch well out on a branch only a few feet above her.

She swung to and fro, and the bunch kept coming in range of her eyes. Suddenly she realized that this was somehow different from all the knots she had examined. It was such a pretty knot she decided she would like to have it to put in her room. She got a stepladder and climbed up. As her eyes came level with it, something darted almost in her face and was gone. "Oh!" she cried. And again, "Oh!" She was looking into the daintiest, softest little cup, no bigger than a fifty-cent piece, and in it were two tiny white eggs. It was a hummingbird's nest.

Carefully Sue touched it with a finger. It was firm but unbelievably soft. As a house is sometimes shingled over the entire outside, so this tiny nest was covered on the outside with lichens. So skillfully had these been put on that the material of which the nest was made was completely hidden until she peeked inside.

"Are there eggs or young?" asked Tommy, coming up behind her.

"Eggs!" replied Sue. "Tommy, it's the loveliest thing I've ever seen. What is it made of? Where did Mrs. Hummer ever find anything so soft? And how did she stick those lichens on? What — "

"Hey, cut off the power and put on the brakes!" replied Tommy. "One thing at a time. Then we won't get all mixed up. Is that nest sort of brownish inside?"

Sue said it was. "I thought so," Tommy continued. "It's made mostly of fern cotton, that soft brown stuff you find on the stem of some ferns. Anyway, it's plant down of some kind. Those lichens she has shingled the outside with are fastened on with spider silk and she has used that in binding the cup and fastening the nest to the tree. Silk is pretty strong, you know. Now you'd better get down. You don't want to worry Mrs. Hummer. You might make her desert her nest."

In a jiffy Sue was down, crying, "I wouldn't do that for the world! There she is now!"

Sure enough, Mrs. Hummer had waited only long enough for them to move away a few feet before darting over to her precious nest. Directly above it she stopped for a second or two in midair, then dropped into the dainty little cup.

"When do you suppose those eggs will hatch?" Sue wanted to know.

"If I knew when she began sitting on them I could tell you. Not knowing, I couldn't even guess. We'll just have to watch," replied Tommy.

So every day the stepladder was taken out and Sue or Sammy or Tommy peeped into the nest. On the tenth day there were no eggs but two squirming mites that Sammy insisted were more like bugs than birds. They grew fast as all bird babies do. Mrs. Hummer was a busy little mother.

Apparently she had no help from Mr. Hummer. In fact he wasn't seen anywhere around the place.

Sue spent a lot of time watching the little family. From the size of honeybees, the babies grew until they so completely filled the nest that it seemed one or the other must soon be crowded out. Sue discovered that they had short bills instead of long ones like their mother. Then one day she had a good view of a baby being fed. The baby opened its mouth wide in the way most baby birds do. Mother thrust her long bill down the little throat until Sue was afraid the baby would be choked to death. She was really alarmed.

"It's dreadful! It must hurt the poor little things," she protested.

"You haven't seen any tears running down their faces," Tommy teased.

Sue glared at him. "How would you like to have something long and sharp run way down your throat when you opened your mouth because you were hungry?" she demanded.

"First rate if I had a throat made for it," replied Tommy, "and that was the only way I could get my food. They are fed by regurgitation."

"Meaning what?" demanded Sammy, who had been listening.

"Feeding with partly digested food. Pigeons feed their squabs that way. The squab pokes its head into the mother's mouth and finds the food she has pumped up into her throat. A baby hummingbird can't do that because of its mother's long bill, so it simply opens its mouth wide and mother pokes her long bill down baby's throat and pumps the food straight to where it will do the most good," explained Tommy.

"That may do for pigeons and hummingbirds, but I don't want my food pumped into me. I couldn't taste it," said Sammy.

23

The Paper Makers

"What are you watching this time?" asked Sammy as he joined his cousin.

"Some paper makers getting their pulp wood. I've been wondering where they were getting it. Now I know," replied Tommy.

"Paper makers! What paper makers? Look out for those hornets, Tommy! You'll get stung if you don't watch out. Where are your paper makers? I don't see any," replied Sammy.

"You're looking straight at them. Something the matter with your eyes, Sammy?" retorted Tommy.

Just then Sue joined them. "I know!" she cried. "It's those hornets, isn't it, Tommy? Why do you call them paper makers?"

"Because that's just what they are. I suppose you know what paper is made of?" replied Tommy.

"Some is made from rags and some is made from

wood ground into pulp. The rag paper is the best kind," said Sammy, a bit proud of his knowledge.

"That depends on what you want it for," replied Tommy. "Anyway, pulp paper came first, and hornets or wasps, for that is what they really are, made it long before man knew how. I guess they were the very first paper makers."

"Cut the riddles, Tommy, and tell us what you're driving at," retorted Sammy impatiently. "There goes one of those hornets, and there goes the other. It's good riddance I say. I don't like them. I don't want to be stung. Now what about this paper making? It doesn't make sense to me."

Tommy's grin was provoking but infectious. "Don't worry about being stung; their nest isn't around here, and as long as you don't bother them they won't bother you," said he. "You wait here a few minutes. Those two will come back or some others will. That piece of wood they were on has been dead so long that the bark fell off long ago. It's gray from exposure to the weather but isn't rotted. It's their pulpwood. Here comes one now. Watch her closely."

The wasp flew straight to the piece of dead wood and began to walk about on it. Apparently she was examining the surface with care. Still a bit uncertain and fearful, Sue and Sammy went near enough to watch closely. At first they couldn't make out what she was about. It was Sue who finally saw what was going on. She stared in wide-eyed surprise.

"Why, I do believe she's eating that wood! Anyway she's biting it. Is she really eating it, Tommy? If she isn't, what's she doing?" Sue cried.

Tommy laughed as he replied, "Didn't I tell you she's a paper maker? She's biting off tiny bits of that gray outer wood. She will chew it into pulp and mix it with some secretion in her mouth that will make it into paper. Here comes another!"

Sammy scowled as they watched the busy workers. "Look at those stingers! I don't like them! Boy, how they could hurt!"

"Don't worry," replied Tommy. "If you don't bother them they won't bother you. Just keep away from their home."

"That's easy, seeing that I don't know where it is," retorted Sammy.

"What do they want that paper for?" asked Sue.

"Follow me and perhaps I can show you. Seeing is believing, you know," replied Tommy.

He had taken note of the direction in which the wasps had flown and now led the way. He walked slowly, stopping frequently to look ahead carefully. The others followed, looking too but not knowing what they were looking for. It wasn't very exciting, but it was fun. They had gone some distance when Tommy stopped and pointed to a tree at the edge of the woods.

"Do you see that big, gray, pear-shaped thing up there in the tree? Well, that's it. That's what we have been looking for," Tommy explained.

"Meaning just what?" demanded Sammy.

"That's the home of those hornets, and it's made of the paper you saw them making," replied Tommy. "For a long time I have wondered why the big nests of the white-faced hornets, as these wasps are called, are always that soft gray. Now I know. It's because the pulp is made of that weathered old wood. Of course the paper of the nest is the same color as the pulp."

"I'm going to throw a stick up there and try to knock that nest down," said Sammy, looking about for a stick.

"Oh, no you're not!" replied Tommy. "Just remember those stingers."

"If that's made of nothing but paper I should think that in wet weather it would get all soft and fall to pieces," said Sue thoughtfully.

"It doesn't," said Tommy, shaking his head. "It seems to be waterproof. Water rolls off it as it does off a duck's back. There are several layers of it in the walls of the nest, and no matter how hard it rains the inmates are always dry. That nest is the biggest one I have seen in a long time, but it was wholly built this summer. There must be a big family in there by this time."

"Isn't it a colony, not just a family?" inquired Sue.

"No. This is what I would call strictly a family affair," said Tommy.

"What do you mean by family affair?" Sammy wanted to know.

"Just that, one big family," said Tommy. He went on to explain: "Last fall, somewhere, somehow, Mother Wasp found shelter and lived through the winter. As soon as it was warm enough this spring she started a new home. First she hunted for the right kind of wood. From it she made pulp and then paper. This was made into a few cells, like the wax cells of honeycomb. In each she placed an egg. As soon as these hatched and the young were big enough, they helped make more cells and put a covering over them. More cells meant more eggs, more eggs more young, more young more workers and more workers more room needed. Then Mother could devote all her time to household duties, laying eggs and raising more children to make the home bigger. It grew from the size of a baseball to what you see up there now. So you see it really is a family affair."

"I'm still puzzled," declared Sue, and she looked it. "I don't yet see how they do it. I should think they would have to first make the outside the size they want and fill it with cells afterward."

"I don't know myself exactly how it's done," admitted Tommy. "The walls are of several layers, and I suppose they somehow tear away from the inside while adding to the outside. So it grows with more room inside and always a roof. They are very clever. Don't you think so?"

"Well, with this big home this year they'll have a good start for next year," said Sue.

"Not those babies," declared Tommy. "The fact is, you may have that nest after cold weather sets in if you want it. I'll cut it down for you then."

"And have a lot of hornets come pouring out when we get where it's warm? No thanks!" Sammy spoke up.

"Nothing of the sort," replied his cousin with a shake of his head. "Only the mothers-to-be, like the queen bumblebees, will live through the winter. In late fall, before frost, they will leave this nest and find sheltered places where they can sleep all winter, perhaps in a building. All the others will die. When spring comes the sleeping mothers will waken and each start a new family home like this one."

"I don't see what fun they have in living. All they do is work and die," said Sammy.

"There can be a lot of fun in work if you look for it," retorted Tommy. "How about this nest, Sue? Do you want it? If you do I'll get it for you as soon as it's deserted in the fall."

"Oh, Tommy, I'd love to have it if you're sure the wasps won't want it," replied Sue.

"They won't. It's as good as yours right now," declared Tommy.

"It will be a lovely souvenir of this summer," added Sue.

24

Living Jewels

There are jewels and jewels. When we mention jewels we usually have in mind certain precious stones. They are without life despite the fires that seem to live in some of them. But there are jewels that are truly alive. Most of these come from very humble beginnings.

"I don't like worms — ugh!" exclaimed Sue. She had stopped at a milkweed plant and her nose was turned up in disgust.

"That isn't a worm; it's a caterpillar. Caterpillars are not worms at all. They have feet. Worms do not," said Tommy.

"I don't care what it is, it's horrid anyway! It makes me crawl," retorted Sue.

"Don't be silly," protested Tommy. "Some caterpillars are not pretty, but some are. That big greenish-yellow one with black stripes may not be handsome, but it is sort of striking-looking."

"I don't like its looks," insisted Sue.

"Neither do the birds," replied Tommy. "Perhaps that's why Mother Nature dressed it up that way. I guess the birds don't like the taste either, for those that eat caterpillars, even the hairy ones, won't touch the milkweed caterpillar."

"Is that the name of this one?" Sammy asked.

"Folks call it that," said Tommy. "It lives on milkweed leaves. I've never seen it eat anything else."

"Will it turn into a butterfly or a moth?" inquired Sue.

"A butterfly," replied Tommy. "A monarch butterfly and — "

"Does that mean it's a sort of king butterfly?" Sammy interrupted.

"There's one now!" cried Tommy as a large butterfly alighted on a milkweed plant. The wings were a brownish or coppery red bordered with black, and the veins were black. A double row of white spots was set in the black borders, and the tips of the upper wings for a short distance back were black, with a few white and orange spots.

"Don't tell me that that awful caterpillar will

ever be such a handsome butterfly as that!" cried
Sue.

"It sure will, Sue," replied Tommy. "What is
more, it won't wait to be a butterfly before becoming beautiful. It first will become a lovely living
jewel."

Right away Sue and Sammy wanted to know
what he meant by that. "Well," said he, "there are
four stages in a butterfly's life. First it's an egg.
Then — "

"It's a caterpillar," Sue broke in.

"And then it's a something or other in a cocoon,"
said Sammy.

Tommy shook his head. "You're wrong, but you
have the right idea," said he. "It's moths, not butterflies, that come out of cocoons. Moth caterpillars
spin cocoons of silk and in them become pupae, the
'something or other' you mentioned, Sammy. The
pupa of a butterfly gets along without the silken
covering of a cocoon and becomes a chrysalis. From
this it changes to a butterfly, and this is the fourth
stage."

Suddenly Sue fairly shrieked with delight. "See,
Tommy, what I found! It's a piece of jewelry, an
eardrop, only of course it isn't really. What is it,
Tommy?" She held out a leaf from which, sus-

pended from the middle, was something that indeed did resemble a lovely jeweled eardrop or small pendant. It was green, the upper part dark and gradually shading to a lighter tone on the lower part. It looked as if it might have been carved from a piece of lovely jade. Around the upper part was a fine band of shining gold, and a few tiny flecks of gold were scattered on the lower part. The whole thing was exquisite. It was no wonder that Sue had shrieked with delight.

"That's the living jewel I mentioned," said Tommy. "It's the chrysalis of a monarch butterfly. I am so glad you found it, Sue. That was once a caterpillar just like the one over there that you think is so awful."

Sue looked at the big monarch butterfly lazily

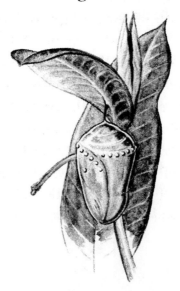

flying about as if it hadn't a care in the world, as at that time it probably hadn't. She looked at the living jewel in her hand, then back at the butterfly, and drew a long breath. "You are beautiful as you are, but you were even more lovely as you were," said she softly.

"Not always," smiled Tommy, nodding toward the awful caterpillar eating a milkweed leaf.

Sue made a face. "It doesn't seem possible that anything so lovely could come from anything so horrid. It's hard to believe," said she.

"No more so than to believe that the butterfly flying where he pleases was ever a motionless yet living jewel like the one in your hand," replied Tommy.

Sue, being nothing if not honest, practically admitted the truth of this. "I guess," said she, "that things we see often we just don't think anything about, and so don't really see and know them. Ever since I can remember I have seen butterflies but never have given them a thought. A butterfly has been just a butterfly and nothing more. It never has reminded me of caterpillars, nor have caterpillars reminded me of butterflies. But they will from now on. Whenever I see a caterpillar I'll wonder what it will be like when it's a butterfly."

"Or a moth," suggested Tommy.

"Or a moth," agreed Sue, smiling. "And when I see a butterfly — "

"Or moth," interposed Tommy.

"I'll wonder what it looked like when it was a caterpillar," Sue finished.

Sammy was watching the caterpillar eating the leaf. "Some appetite," said he. "Seems queer to think of that thing sprouting wings and flying about."

"It doesn't sprout wings exactly; it changes all over, you know," said Tommy.

"I know," replied Sammy. "It sort of starts life all over again. I guess that's more wonderful than if it really did sprout wings."

"I wonder why they named that butterfly monarch?" inquired Sue.

"You've got me," confessed Tommy. "Perhaps because it's so independent and such a great traveler someone thought of it as monarch of all it surveys. It sure does survey a lot in its short lifetime."

"Does that mean it flies about more than other butterflies?" asked Sammy. Then he added, "Even if it does, that can't be much. At best it can't travel far."

"Don't fool yourself," retorted Tommy. "That

butterfly we've been watching either spent last winter way down in the sunny South, perhaps in Florida, and returned this spring, or it is this year's butterfly and will spend next winter down South and return next summer."

"Tommy Brown, are you telling the truth?" demanded Sue.

"Cross my heart," replied Tommy, and did it.

"You're spoofing us. No butterfly lives long enough for that, or could fly that distance," declared Sammy.

"Believe it or not, the monarch can and does," retorted Tommy, a bit heatedly. He resented being doubted. "In the fall monarchs gather and migrate just as the birds do. Like them they make the long journey to the warmth of the sunny South. Birds don't like to eat them any better than when they are caterpillars, so they haven't much to fear but high winds and bad weather. In the spring when they head back North they come as fast as the milkweed plants appear."

"Who told you all that? How do you know so much about it?" Sammy spoke a bit sharply.

Tommy had recovered his good nature. "It's hard to believe, so I don't wonder you're full of doubt," said he. "One fall I saw a lot of these butterflies passing over. It made me curious because it was the first time I had ever seen so many butterflies all of one kind. So I went to the library and read up about them. They make the round trip only once, so when they start South there is none among them to show the way. But most of them get there all right and a lot of them get back again. Isn't that something?"

The others agreed that it was really something and Tommy added, "Mr. Monarch is something of a dandy."

"What do you mean, dandy?" demanded Sammy.

"Just that. He carries perfume," chuckled Tommy.

"Aw now," began Sammy, then held his tongue and Tommy continued.

"It's a fact; he really does. On each of the lower wings is a tiny pocket filled with perfume," explained Tommy.

"What's it for?" demanded Sammy.

"Search me!" replied Tommy. "Perhaps Mrs. Monarch likes it."

Sue drew a long breath. "Of course she does. I think that's nice. It's simply wonderful. Never again will I say 'only a butterfly.' I didn't know that any butterflies lived through the winter," said she.

"One other does, the mourningcloak. In a way it's even more wonderful than the monarch, for it winters over here right in the North, sort of hibernating in some sheltered place the way the queen bumblebee does, and some of the wasps," explained Tommy. "I've seen one out on a mild day in the middle of winter," he added.

25

The Fierce Little One

"The funniest little mouse just ran under those leaves over there, the smallest mouse I've ever seen," cried Sue.

Uncle Ben laughed. "I doubt it was a mouse, my dear. Probably it was a shrew, Teeny Weeny, the littlest one," said he.

"Isn't a shrew a kind of mouse?" Sammy asked.

Uncle Ben shook his head. "No more a mouse than a rat is a rabbit," he stated.

"I wish I could see one close to," said Sue a bit wistfully.

"I guess perhaps that can be arranged," said Uncle Ben. He poked about on a shelf. "I guess this will do," said he, holding up an empty pickle jar.

"Do for what?" asked Sammy curiously.

"To catch Teeny Weeny in," replied Uncle Ben. "Come with me and we'll fix a pitfall for him and hope he'll tumble in."

He led the way over to where a long pole had been on the ground so long that when he lifted it aside it left sort of a sunken little path or runway. Midway along this he dug a hole, just large enough to hold the jar with the open top exactly flush with the bottom of the runway. Overhanging grass was extra thick right there, and the shade of a tree fell across the spot, making it extra dark.

"Now," said Uncle Ben, "we will go away for a while. We may not catch Teeny Weeny this afternoon, but in the night he very likely will tumble in. You see he dearly loves to scamper along little runways such as this one left by taking up that pole."

"How do you know he'll find it?" questioned Sammy.

"I don't, but I'll be surprised if he doesn't. He has to do a lot of running about to find enough food, and sooner or later he'll find this nice little path, run along it and tumble in," explained Uncle Ben.

When they left for home the pickle jar was still empty. Right after breakfast the next morning they raced over to Uncle Ben's. He saw them coming and held up the pickle jar. In it was a tiny restless little prisoner.

"If I hadn't been told what he is I would have thought him a baby mouse with an awfully sharp nose," declared Sue.

"Don't tell me that an animal as small as that is fully grown!" exclaimed Sammy.

"It is, absolutely. It is among animals what the hummingbird is among birds — smallest," said Uncle Ben.

"And with the biggest appetite," added Tommy, who had joined them.

"Yes," said Uncle Ben. "Considering what happened in this jar last night and his big appetite, I am glad that he is no bigger than he is. It was a tragedy."

"What happened?" chorused the three.

Uncle Ben looked grave. "Before going to bed last night I visited our pitfall and found that two shrews had fallen into it. I brought the jar into the house. The two captives were the same size. In the morning when I looked I could see only one, but both were there in the jar. They still are," said Uncle Ben.

There was a startled look in Sue's eyes. "You mean . . . ?" she began and stopped.

"I mean that that little fellow there is a cannibal. Those two had a great fight, and because he was starving the winner ate the loser," declared Uncle Ben.

"How could he have been starving?" demanded Sammy.

"Because his appetite is so enormous and he digests his food so rapidly, that according to a noted scientist a shrew probably needs about his own weight in food every twenty-four hours. Without any food he would starve to death in less than a day," was the astonishing reply.

"It was my fault," continued Uncle Ben. "I should have remembered what nervous, quick-tempered little fellows they were and should have separated them. Now you know what I meant when I said that Teeny Weeny has one of the greatest appetites in the world. He is a wee savage, and with such an appetite it's good that he is no bigger than he is."

"Just suppose," said Sue, "that he was as big as a lion or tiger!"

"As big as that, and with such an appetite as he now has, he would be the most terrible creature that ever lived," said Uncle Ben.

"Just suppose we had to eat our own weight in

food every day, or suppose he was as big as a whale," contributed Sammy.

Uncle Ben laughed. "Suppose we stop supposing and consider the shrew as he is," said he. "As he is he's more marvelous than he possibly could be as big as you have been supposing him to be. See what a mite of a fellow he is, yet he has all the bones, muscles and organs that larger animals have. He hunts for his food, fights, and tries to avoid his enemies, just as larger animals do. He looks out for himself without help from anyone. He lives just as others do, yet he is so small that he weighs less than fifty grains. You know it takes seven thousand grains to make a pound."

"Some difference between a shrew and a whale," remarked Sammy. "How big is a whale, anyway?"

"That depends on the kind of whale. The biggest

one, the blue or sulphur-bottom whale, is not only the largest living animal but probably the largest that ever has lived," replied Uncle Ben.

"How big?" asked Sammy.

"Of course it varies. There have been some well over a hundred feet long. Such a one might weigh a hundred and twenty-five to a hundred and fifty tons," replied Uncle Ben.

"Gee, what a lot of shrews it would take to make a whale," put in Sammy, and everybody laughed.

"There's a problem for you to work out," said Uncle Ben. "We'll say that a shrew weighs forty grains. For convenience in figuring we'll pick a big whale, say one of one hundred and fifty tons. A ton is two thousand pounds and a grain is a seven thousandth part of a pound. Now go to it and see who gets the answer first," said Uncle Ben. "Just keep in mind that both are mammals, each as perfect as the other."

For a few minutes pencils were busy. Then Tommy came up with the answer that 52,500,000 shrews equal a whale.

"Oh my goodness, that can't be right!" declared Sue.

"It is though," declared Sammy, checking his own figures. He turned to Uncle Ben. "You said that both are perfect mammals. It seems to me that the shrew is more perfect. He has four legs and the whale hasn't any."

"It isn't necessary to have four legs to be a perfect mammal," explained Uncle Ben. "Man has only two legs, but he is a perfect mammal. Walking upright he has need for only two, so arms have been given him in place of the other two. A whale has no possible use for legs or arms. In place of arms he has a pair of paddles, or flippers. Instead of legs he has a powerful tail with flukes to drive him through the water. Mammals that never leave the water have no use for legs, but have been given aids to swimming. So they are just as perfect as those with legs."

"I have heard that a shrew's eyes are no good. If that's true I don't think it's a perfect mammal," ventured Tommy, and Sue nodded in agreement.

Uncle Ben admitted that all the eyes of a shrew are good for is to tell light from darkness. "Shrews live where there is so little light that they have no use for eyes so far as seeing things is concerned. They have all they need to live the kind of life they are intended to live. What more could be asked? Now we'll take Teeny Weeny out and let him go. With that tremendous appetite he must be starving right now, even if he did eat his own weight last night," said Uncle Ben.

"Imagine a hundred-ton whale eating another hundred-ton whale," chuckled Sue.

"What does a whale eat, anyway?" Sammy asked.

"You'd be surprised," laughed Uncle Ben. "The kind we've been talking about, the biggest one, lives mostly on some of the smallest creatures in the sea, so tiny that one almost needs a microscope to see them. They are in great masses and are called plankton. For that kind of food no teeth are needed. So this big whale has none. Hanging from the roof of the mouth are plates of what is called whalebone although it isn't true bone. These plates end in long hair-like fringes. The whale swims with mouth open through a mass of this plankton and these fringes strain out the plankton to be swallowed without the water. So it is that the smallest mammal sometimes kills others his own size or bigger for food, and the biggest one lives on tiny creatures almost too small to be seen. It's a wonderful world we live in if we have eyes to see it."

"And I thought it was going to be stupid out here in the country," muttered Sammy as the three made their way homeward.

26

Some Hair!

The twins had grown fond of Uncle Ben. They liked to visit him, for they knew they were always welcome, and they were sure of good stories and much of interest that was new to them. Late one afternoon they dropped in to see him. They were sitting out in front of the cabin when suddenly Lightfoot the Deer stepped out into the little clearing.

For perhaps a full minute the buck stood with head held high staring at the little group watching him. Presently he lowered his head and began to browse, snatching a mouthful here and a mouthful there, flicking his tail from time to time. Gradually he worked his way around the clearing. Suddenly he threw up his head as if startled. For a few seconds he stood motionless, his slender nose held high. Then, as if he had springs in his feet, he

bounded away, head up and tail stiffly erect, showing only the underside so that it seemed to be all
white. His branch of the family is known as the
white-tailed deer.

"What frightened him?" Sammy asked.

Uncle Ben chuckled. "You or Sue, or both of
you did," said he.

"I didn't so much as wiggle a finger," said
Sammy indignantly. Sue was equally insistent that
she hadn't moved.

Uncle Ben wet a finger and held it up. "I
thought so," said he. "There is just a faint breeze
blowing from us to where he was and that marvelous nose of his told him that there were strangers
here, and strangers are never to be trusted. Anyway, that's the way the woodland folk feel. That
buck knows me but he doesn't know you. Perhaps
he will before you go back to the city. Just now he
is nervous and easily frightened."

"Why now any more than any other time?"
asked Sue.

"Because he doesn't feel too well, and he won't
until those antlers of his are fully grown," said Uncle Ben.

"I suppose you mean his horns," said Sammy.

Uncle Ben smiled. "I mean his antlers, Sammy.

Some Hair!

It always seems to me a bit queer how people persist in using the wrong names for things when it's just as easy to call them by their right names. Cows have horns. So do rams and goats. All male members of the deer family have antlers. These are very different from horns. The latter are hollow and are permanent. Antlers are solid, bony, and they last only a few months. I mean that they last on the heads of their owners only a few months. Then they drop off and new ones grow. Perhaps you've noticed that that buck's antlers have no sharp points such as they will have in the fall."

"I did," replied Sue. "They're covered with a sort of skin that looks like velvet."

Uncle Ben nodded. "When they are in this stage they are said to be in the velvet," said he. "Come in the house with me now."

He led the way inside. From a table he picked up a single antler having five points, or tines. "Old Lightfoot wore this last fall," said he. "I found it in the spring where he dropped it last winter. It's half of his last year's crown, or set of weapons, whichever you please. The other half is out there in the woods somewhere. Feel how hard this is and look at the size of it, then remember that it started as just a little knob on that buck's head and in a few short months grew to be what you see here. It grew just as a plant does. When I think of this I have a funny little feeling of awe, as if I were looking at something produced by true magic. Yet I've met people who can see nothing wonderful in nature."

"I think," ventured Sammy, "that Old Mother Nature, while wonderful, is stupid about some things."

"What for instance?" asked Uncle Ben, the laugh wrinkles gathering about his eyes.

"Well," replied Sammy, "when she has grown a set of big antlers for a deer why doesn't she let him keep them? Why does she bother with growing a new set every year? It seems to me like a lot of wasted effort, not to mention making it mighty uncomfortable for the deer in hot weather. If it's uncomfortable for old Lightfoot, what must it be for a moose when he grows a set of those tremendous antlers he wears?"

Uncle Ben was smiling. "I have thought about that myself," said he. "I can recall when, like you, Sammy, I wondered if Old Mother Nature wasn't a bit stupid in this matter. But when I began to become really acquainted with the deer folk I began to see reasons why antlers are taken away from the bucks every winter and new ones grown through the summer. They may not be the real reasons but they are good enough for me."

"Tell us what they are. Please do. If they are good enough for you they are good enough for us, so please tell us," said Sue.

"A buck's antlers are his weapons. When they are hardened and polished he feels pretty chesty. He feels high, as they say. He wants to use those antlers. He goes about with a chip on his shoulder. He is spoiling for a fight. He goes out of his way to pick a quarrel. Having those splendid weapons he wants to use them, so he goes looking for trouble. Man is very much like that. When he has great armies and navies he is very likely to want to use them and so we have wars. There is such a thing as being too well armed." Uncle Ben's face was very sober and his eyes had a faraway look. He paused for a moment, then continued: "As I said, a buck likes to fight for the fun of fighting. Also, Lightfoot likes to show off before Mrs. Lightfoot to win her admiration, and having won it to keep it.

"But Old Mother Nature knows that it would not do to have this hot-blooded, hot-tempered fellow going about through the forest looking for trouble the year round. It wouldn't do at all. She knows too that those unarmed do not go about looking for trouble. They try to avoid it. A buck, having fought for a mate and won her, no longer has use for his weapons. So Old Mother Nature takes them away from him to keep him out of trouble, and from making trouble for others.

"In the late spring and early summer Mrs. Deer wants to be alone with her babies. It's better and safer for her and for them that Lightfoot should be away from them. So Old Mother Nature starts a new set of antlers growing on the buck's head. Because these grow so fast, as they must be ready for fall, they take much of his strength and he feels so uncomfortable that he wants to be alone. He goes off by himself where he can be quiet and undisturbed and where those tender and sensitive antlers are less likely to be injured. So perhaps Old Mother Nature isn't stupid after all."

"I'll say she isn't," declared Sammy with conviction, and to this Sue agreed.

"Didn't you look for the mate to this antler when you found it?" Sue asked.

"Yes, my dear. I looked for quite a distance around. The trouble was that they didn't fall at the same time," replied Uncle Ben.

"I had an idea that they were joined together, sort of all one thing," said Sammy.

Some Hair!

"No indeed. They are separate just as the ears and the eyes are separate. When the time comes, Lightfoot loses his antlers one at a time just the way you lost your first teeth. The second antler may drop very soon after the first, or it may be hours later, even the next day, before it becomes loose enough to fall. Meanwhile Lightfoot isn't standing still. So it is that sometimes the second one drops off a long way from where the first one fell," explained Uncle Ben.

"While we are talking about antlers and horns there is something I want to know about horns, or one kind anyway that is called a horn," said Sammy.

"What kind is that?" asked Uncle Ben.

"The horn that the rhinoceros carries on his snout," replied Sammy.

"Just what is it you want to know about it?" asked Uncle Ben.

"I want to know if it is ivory like the tusks of an elephant," replied Sammy. "If it isn't ivory, what is it? I've wondered about it a good many times."

Uncle Ben chuckled. "You'd be surprised," said he. "An elephant's tusk and a rhinoceros's horn are not the same at all. I suppose you've heard that an elephant's tusk really is a modified tooth."

Sammy nodded. "I've heard that but it doesn't seem possible."

There was a twinkle in the eyes of Uncle Ben. "Old Mother Nature meets the needs of each kind of animal and so the elephant has been given tusks. The rhinoceros doesn't need tusks but it does need a weapon. Instead of a modified tooth, Old Mother Nature has given him that horn, which really is modified hair."

"Now, Uncle Ben! Do give it to us in smaller doses," said Sammy.

"I'll agree it is a pretty big dose to swallow all at once," chuckled Uncle Ben. "What I mean is the horn is composed of the same kind of material as hair. I suppose you might really say it's a solidified mass of hair. I admit it sounds queer but that's what the scientists tell us, and they ought to know."

"Some hair, I'll say," mumbled Sammy.

27

The Masked Raiders

Tommy had just come in from the cornfield. "Corn's in the milk and coons are in the corn, or have been," said he. He held out an ear of corn from which the husks had been partly torn back. Sharp teeth had taken a couple of bites from the exposed kernels, which were in the milky stage — not quite fully mature.

"Coons?" questioned Sammy as if sure he had not heard correctly.

"Coons!" repeated Tommy. "Raccoons. They can do a lot of mischief in a cornfield. How about a little excitement tonight? The moon rises early and will be full tonight. It will be almost as light as day. If you say so we'll take the dogs and have a coon hunt. What do you say?"

"You mean hunt them to kill?" Sue asked.

"Sue, you ought to know me better than to ask

that," said Tommy reproachfully. "We'll give those coons a scare and drive them out of the corn. You may have a chance to see one or more in the moonlight."

"Do you think there'll be more than one?" Sammy wanted to know.

"From the looks of the corn I'd guess there was a whole family there last night, and I'm sure they'll be back again tonight. Coons are crazy for corn when it's in the milk and will go a long distance to get it," said Tommy.

When the moon was high enough that evening to light the landscape almost as clearly as by day, the three, with old Bowser the Hound and Flip the Terrier, headed for the cornfield. As they drew near it Bowser began to bark. He had found a trail.

Now over in the corn were five half-grown young raccoons and their parents. At the sound of the dog's voice, the mother and father started to round up the youngsters, who were scattered through the corn. One of the young ones started to run. In a panic the others followed. They were running headlong through the corn.

"My goodness! It sounds like a herd of hogs," cried Tommy. "We can't run through the corn without breaking it down, so we'll beat it for the lower end of the field and perhaps head the rascals off. Come on!"

What with the barking of the dogs in the corn and the yelling of the young folk outside racing to head off the coons, it was very exciting. For the five young coons it was very frightening. For the first time they were running for their lives. They lost their heads completely. They could think of nothing but running and finding a tree to climb. They were so frightened they had no idea of the direction in which they were running. Mother and Father Coon ran too, trying to get control of the panic-stricken children.

When the young coons broke out of the cornfield they were not headed for the woods as they should have been, but were right out on the open meadow, where by now it was as light as day. Now Mother Coon pushed ahead and took the lead, knowing that the others would follow. She headed for the near-est tree, a big hickory over near the Smiling Pool. There they would at least be safe from the dogs. When they got there she sent the youngsters up the tree; probably she told them to stay there. She didn't stay. She headed for a not too distant alder swamp. Tommy, Sue and Sammy came around the corner of the cornfield just in time to see Father

Coon hurrying after Mother. He had seen her at the hickory tree and understood what she was about. The dogs would follow her trail away from the tree over to the swamp. He took a shortcut to join her.

It worked out just that way. The two big coons waited in the swamp. It was too warm for long running. Anyway, with the youngsters safe they would rather fight than run. Both were good fighters. Bowser and Flip were so intent on following the fresh scent that they almost ran into the two coons before they saw them. The coons didn't wait to be attacked. They started the fight, and what a fight that was! The sound of it rolled out of the swamp and across to the big hickory tree, high in which the five young coons clung, shivering with excitement and fright as they listened. The sound brought Tommy and his cousins on the run to the edge of the swamp. There they stopped.

"It's dreadful!" cried Sue, her voice tremulous. "Those dogs will kill that poor coon, and I don't want him killed."

"Don't worry," said Tommy. "By the sounds I should say there are two raccoons there, and both big old ones, good fighters. They are quite able to take care of themselves. Otherwise I would have stopped them before now. All I wanted was to drive the coons out of the cornfield and scare them so they would stay away from it. Here comes Flip now. He's had enough. The scamp is no coward, but this time he has met more than his match and he knows it."

Sure enough, Flip was backing out of the bushes. He wasn't running away. He wasn't turning tail. He was making an honorable retreat, acknowledging that he was beaten but refusing to run. For just a second Mrs. Coon poked her head out of the bushes to snarl at Flip. Meanwhile Bowser and Father Coon were fighting desperately, snarling and growling, with Bowser yelping when he felt the coon's sharp teeth. One would be on top, then the other. Bowser was a good fighter, big, strong, unafraid. This was equally true of the coon. Locked together, they rolled in the black mud of the swamp until they were a sight. Finally they rolled into the brook that ran through the swamp. This separated them. Bowser scrambled out on one bank and the big coon on the other. They shook themselves, then glared across the brook at each other. Bowser turned away. Enough is always enough and he had had enough. The coon looked as if he felt the same way about it.

It had been an exciting experience for Sue and Sammy, and on their way home their tongues flew as they talked it over. "Why don't you shoot or trap those coons, Tommy? I would if they were ruining my corn," said Sammy.

Tommy looked at Sammy with an odd little smile as if he felt a little embarrassed. "I suppose you will think I'm softhearted, but the truth is I'm fond of those rascals," said he. "They do get into mischief, and do some damage sometimes. But they don't know it's mischief. To them this is a free world and they have as much right to that corn as I have. It's like that with all the wild folk. I don't want to hurt any of them."

"I wonder what makes birds and animals wild, anyway," ventured Sue.

"Fear," replied Tommy promptly. "Just fear."

"Do you mean that if they were not afraid of us they wouldn't be wild?" asked Sammy.

"That's it," replied Tommy earnestly. "They wouldn't be what we call wild, and they wouldn't hate us. Fear leads to hate. Take away fear and the wild things are no longer wild. They are friendly and willing to trust us. I guess trust is right next to love."

As three tired coon hunters went to bed, Sammy said, "It was better than TV or the movies." And he sounded as if he really meant it. It was one more of the happy memories that Sue and Sammy took home with them at the end of a vacation which had completely reversed its frustrating start.

Index

Index

Bottles, mud, and potter wasp, 135–138. *See also* Cells; Holes; Nests; Pits

Bullhead, 85–88

CATAMOUNT. *See* Mountain lion

Caterpillar, 213–215, 217–218; and potter wasp, 135–139. *See also* Milkweed caterpillar

Catfish. *See* Bullhead

Cave-dweller wasp. *See* Mud-dauber wasp

Cells, leaf, and leaf-cutter bee, 133–134; mud, and mud-dauber wasp, 140–142. *See also* Bottles; Holes; Nests; Pits

Chain of life, 138–139, 156–160, 162

Chipmunk, 12–21, 44

Chrysalis, and butterfly, 215

Cliff, and raven, 148

Cocoon, and moth, 215

Copperhead, 50

Coral snake, 50

Corn, 239–240

Cottonmouth moccasin, 50

Cougar. *See* Mountain lion

Crown, 233. *See also* Antlers, deer

DEER, white-tailed, 8, 152–153, 160–161, 230–237. *See also* Antlers, deer

Dogs: Bruce, 42–43; Flip the Terrier, 107–109, 178–180, 240–244; Bowser the Hound, 240–241

EGGS, and bees, 105–106; and butterflies, 215; and hummingbirds, 200–202; and lace-winged flies, 196; and leaf-cutter bees, 133–134; and mud-dauber wasps, 142; and

paper-maker wasps, 210–211; and potter wasps, 137; and
pumpkin seed fish, 84; and toads, 73; and turtles, 73–79,
80–82. *See also* Bottles; Cells; Holes; Nests; Pits
Eyes, pumpkin seed fish, 84; shrew, 228; snake, 68; toad,
56–57

FEAR, 245; and bees, 102; and ruffed grouse, 173
Feathers, ruffed grouse, 173
Fern cotton, and hummingbird nest, 201
Fish, 80–88; and mink, 153. *See also* Bullhead; Pumpkin
seed; Trout
Flight, of hummingbirds, 197–198
Flippers, and mammals, 228
Fly, and pitcher plant, 29. *See also* Lace-winged fly; Gauzy
Wings; Water fly
FOOD, 47, 138–139, 229; and spider web, 47; and storage for
winter, 15; and toads, 58; and snapping turtles, 73. *See
also names of individual animals;* Pitcher plant
Footprints, 81–82, 163
Fox, 174–186
Freedom, and woods animals (young fox), 181–182, 185–
186
Frog, 157–159; and raccoons, 155; and toads, 60

GARDENS, and toads, 58
Garter snake, 50
Gauzy Wings, 193–194. *See also* Ant lion
Gray marmot. *See* Marmot
Great horned owl (Hooty), 162

HABITAT, proper, and woodchuck, 34–36
Hair, and rhinoceros horn, 238
Hare, 99

Index

Lion. *See* Ant lion; Aphid lion; Mountain lion

Index

Index

Trout, 157
Turtle, 76. *See also* Snapping turtle
Tusks, elephant, 237

USEFULNESS OF ANIMALS TO MANKIND: bullhead, 86; skunk,
116; snake, 61; toad, 58; wasp, 139. *See also* Balance of
nature

VELVET. *See* Antlers, deer

WARNING, and beaver, 145
Warts, and toads, 51
Wasp. *See* Mud wasp; Paper-maker wasp; Yellow jacket
wasp
Water fly, 156–157
Weasel. *See* Mink
Web, spider, 44–48; and instinct, 47–48
Whale, 226–227, 229. *See also* Blue whale
Whalebone, 229
Whistler. *See* Marmot
White-faced hornet. *See* Paper-maker wasp
Woodchuck, 14, 31–41
Working bee, 94
Worm, 213

YELLOW JACKET WASP, 114–116
Young, large animals and, 166; bears and, 165–169; birds
and, 202–203; bullheads and, 86–88; deer and, 236; fish
and, 86; foxes and, 178–186; grouse and, 175–176; hummingbirds and, 202–204; pigeons and, 204; pumpkin seed
fish and, 85; rabbits and, 117–124; raccoons and, 240–
243; turtles and, 79